WITN

D1636009

Nuclear Chemistry

TECHNIQUE OF INORGANIC CHEMISTRY

Editors

HANS B. JONASSEN   ARNOLD WEISSBERGER

Advisory Board

F. A. COTTON   D. SEYFERTH

J. W. IRVINE   G. WILKINSON

Nuclear Chemistry

NOAH R. JOHNSON, EUGENE EICHLER
AND G. DAVIS O'KELLEY

TECHNIQUE OF INORGANIC CHEMISTRY

VOLUME II

INTERSCIENCE PUBLISHERS
a division of John Wiley & Sons, New York • London

Foreword to the Series

A renewed interest in inorganic chemistry in the past twenty years has brought about an enormous increase in the amount of research in this field. The numerous unusual synthetic and structural problems encountered have led to many specific manipulative and instrumental techniques. A modern inorganic chemist must be familiar with these methods and techniques in order to be most effective in the pursuit of his research.

The present series of companion volumes to "Technique of Organic Chemistry" is planned to present in a comprehensive manner the various techniques used specifically in inorganic chemistry and radiochemistry. A treatment of the theoretical background and a critical evaluation of the merits and limitations of the techniques are included in each chapter. Within the aims indicated above, the authors were given the freedom to treat their topics in the manner best suited to the various subjects.

The members of the Advisory Board, Drs. F. A. Cotton, J. W. Irvine, D. Seyferth, and G. Wilkinson have been of great help in the launching and planning of this series. Mrs. D. Faber and Mrs. C. E. Richards have rendered excellent clerical aid; the publisher's staff has been most cooperative. To all of them we express our sincere gratitude.

Tulane University   Hans B. Jonassen

Research Laboratories,   Arnold Weissberger
Eastman Kodak Company

Preface

As radioactive tracers came into more frequent use in the late forties, there emerged a number of good books on nuclear chemistry, radiochemistry, tracer applications, and the like. These works so excellently covered the "state of the art" that in the intervening years there have emerged very few book-length publications in this field. But with the passage of fifteen years, the basic physical ideas have matured and broadened, and the techniques have not only become refined but, in many cases, completely changed. Thus, the time seemed ripe for a "new wave" of nuclear chemistry texts.

This particular volume is a part of the "Technique of Inorganic Chemistry" series edited by Hans B. Jonassen and Arnold Weissberger. Initially, it was planned as one chapter in a larger volume. However, as the writing progressed, two things became apparent: First, the predicted length seemed adequate for a single volume; second, there appeared to be sufficient interest in a single volume on this subject among students and workers in a variety of fields.

Although we wrote principally for the student and research worker with little or no previous radioisotope experience, we feel that many sections contain material that should be interesting and valuable even to veteran nuclear chemists. We included no laboratory experiments as we felt this was well provided for in the books by Choppin (G. R. Choppin, *Experimental Nuclear Chemistry*, Prentice-Hall, Englewood Cliffs, N.J., 1961) and by Overman and Clark (R. T. Overman and H. M. Clark, *Radioisotope Techniques*, McGraw-Hill, New York, 1960). Similarly, we have not appended student exercises; instructors of nuclear chemistry courses should look into the older text of Friedlander and Kennedy (G. Friedlander and J. W. Kennedy, *Nuclear and Radiochemistry*, Wiley, New York, 1955), or the recently published book of Harvey (B. G. Harvey, *Introduction to Nuclear Physics and Chemistry*, Prentice-Hall, Englewood Cliffs, N.J., 1962).

The authors would like to express their thanks to the following individuals for helpful discussions and criticism of the manuscript: R. K. Abele, J. L. Blankenship, G. R. Boyd, T. A. Carlson, A. Chetham-Strode, J. W. Cobble, R. L. Ferguson, V. A. McKay, R. K. Sheline, R. J. Silva, J. R. Tarrant, D. E. Troutner, F. J. Walter, and J. W. Winchester.

Noah R. Johnson
Eugene Eichler
G. Davis O'Kelley

Oak Ridge National Laboratory
Oak Ridge, Tennessee
January, 1963

Contents

Volume II

Contents

Technique of Inorganic Chemistry

Nuclear Chemistry

I. INTRODUCTION

Nuclear chemistry had its inception in 1898 with the work of Pierre and Marie Curie. However, it was not until the days of the Manhattan Project that nuclear chemistry really came of age. The field has now evolved into a hybrid discipline bridging chemistry and nuclear physics.

Because nuclear chemistry has both chemical and physical overtones this field is often confused with radiochemistry. It is now generally agreed that nuclear chemistry can be defined as the use of chemical ideas and techniques in research whose fundamental aim is to gain insight into the nuclear processes themselves. On the other hand, radiochemistry involves the use of radioactive species in solving chemical problems. Since there is an ever-increasing number of workers in all fields of chemistry who utilize radioactive tracers, all chemists are potentially radiochemists. Thus, there seems to be no reason to retain radiochemistry as a distinct term.

The methods of a nuclear chemist are those needed by any chemist using radioactivity. In this volume we have tried to delineate the basic techniques of the field, as well as to point out many of the very recent innovations. At the same time, to isolate the techniques from the fundamental principles which govern them is in many cases to destroy their usefulness, and in some instances to jeopardize the value of any experimental data obtained by their use. It is with this attitude that we have attempted to undergird these experimental techniques with many of the pertinent basic principles and theories of nuclear physics.

Some of the important aspects to be covered are as follows: In Section II the statistical nature of and the laws governing radioactive growth and decay are considered. Also included in this section is a discussion on the

1

modes of nuclear decay. The ways in which these radiations interact with matter and give up their energy is the subject of Section III. The mechanisms and physical methods of producing radioactive nuclides are included in Section IV. In Section V consideration is given to chemical separations, both to the factors governing the choice of separation and to separation methods themselves. The success of an experiment which utilizes radioactivity depends to a great extent on the equipment and techniques employed in detecting the radiations and on the way the sources are prepared and mounted. These are the topics of Sections VI and VII, respectively. The first of these two topics is treated in considerable detail with particular emphasis given to recent developments in scintillation spectrometry and semiconductor radiation detectors. In the last section we have attempted to give some hints as to the future of the use of radioactivity.

A truly complete treatment of such a diverse subject is, of course, not possible in a survey such as this; however each Section is amply referenced. There are a number of good nuclear chemistry texts available, but the first book on the subject (and probably still the best) is that of Friedlander and Kennedy, particularly in its 1955 revision (78). It emphasizes physical principles but does discuss techniques. A more recent volume by Overman and Clark (166) emphasizes the techniques aspect and also includes numerous laboratory experiments, as does a very recent volume by Choppin (46).

A catalog of all available nuclear physics texts would be huge, so we mention only four of varying character: Halliday (96) is concise and readable, though not exhaustive; the work by Green (92) represents a much more sophisticated and rigorous approach, and that of Evans (65) gives an even more detailed treatment of a multitude of topics; finally, the three-volume set edited by Segré (202) explores in detail a number of specific subjects.

Although the scope of this volume does not include the specific details of chemical applications of radioactivity, this subject is covered in the book edited by Wahl and Bonner (226). Of course their reference lists are now ten years old and should be supplemented by searching the current literature. Finally, there is an extremely handy compilation known as *Source Material for Radiochemistry* (211) containing bibliographies of many of the subjects included in this volume.

II. RADIOACTIVE DECAY

1. Radioactive Decay Laws

A. EXPONENTIAL LAW OF DECAY AND "ACTIVITY"

Nuclear decay can be considered as the transformation of one nuclear state into another. The process is a statistical one since in a given short time interval, the probability λ that a particular atom of a radioactive element will disintegrate is independent of its past history and the environmental factors such as temperature and pressure. (It is now known, however, that in certain cases where the radioactive element undergoes decay by capturing orbital electrons, the rate of decay can be altered slightly by changing the electron density around the nucleus.)

For a large number of radioactive nuclei, the rate at which the transformations occur, dN/dt, is proportional to the number, N, of unchanged atoms that are present at any time t. Expressed in differential form the rate of radioactive decay is

$$- dN/dt = \lambda N \tag{1}$$

which is simply the rate law for a first order reaction. Upon integrating, we obtain the exponential law of radioactive decay

$$N = N_0 e^{-\lambda t} \tag{2}$$

where N is the number of unchanged atoms at time t, N_0 is the original number of nuclei at $t = 0$, and λ is a decay constant characteristic of a particular radioactive species. This decay constant, λ, represents the probability per unit of time that a radioactive disintegration will occur.

In general it is not practical to measure directly the number of atoms N or the absolute value of dN/dt, i.e., the *disintegration rate* N_D (sometimes referred to as the *activity*), for a radioactive material. Instead, the *counting rate* **R**, a quantity proportional to λN, is usually determined. (It should be pointed out, however, that direct measurement of dN/dt has become feasible with such techniques as 4π beta counting and liquid scintillation counting.) The over-all detection efficiency of the system, or *counting yield*, ϵ, for a given radioactivity will depend on the type and energy of radiation involved, the nature of the detection instrument, the geometrical arrangement of sample and detector, and the physical nature of the radioactive source itself. We may therefore write for the counting rate

$$\mathbf{R} = \epsilon \lambda N = \epsilon(- dN/dt) \tag{3}$$

with the result that the decay law becomes

$$\mathbf{R} = \mathbf{R}_0 e^{-\lambda t} \tag{4}$$

A term in widespread usage is *specific activity*, which unfortunately means different things to different people. As pointed out by Tolbert and Siri (221), there are at least three common definitions for it: (1) specific activity (gram-element) defined as the disintegration rate of a specific isotope per gram of the element present; (2) specific activity (isotope), the disintegration rate of a given isotope per gram of that isotope; (3) specific activity, the disintegration rate of a radioactive isotope per unit mass of the sample. The last definition is most versatile and, therefore, will be the one adhered to in this chapter.

A point worth re-emphasizing is that disintegration rate and activity, which are indicated by N_D, are synonymous and indicate the actual rate at which radioactive transformations in a given sample are occurring; the counting rate **R** for the same sample will likely be a very different quantity as a result of the less than 100% efficiency of the detection system.

The most common unit of radioactivity is the *curie* (C.), which is 3.700 $\times$ 10^{10} disintegrations per second. Useful submultiples are the *millicurie* (mC.) and the *microcurie* (μC.). A less frequently used unit of radioactive disintegration rate is the *rutherford*, 10^6 disintegrations per second.

B. HALF-LIFE

The rate of radioactive decay is conveniently described in terms of half-life $t_{1/2}$, the time required for an initial number of atoms to be reduced to one-half the number by nuclear transformations. Thus, for time $t = t_{1/2}$ and $N = N_0/2$, equation 2 when expressed in logarithmic form becomes

$$\ln\left(\frac{1}{2}\right) = -\lambda t_{1/2}$$

or

$$t_{1/2} = (\ln 2)/\lambda = 0.693/\lambda \tag{5}$$

Instead of measuring λ, a very convenient way of determining the half-life of a given radioactive species is to plot the logarithm of the activity

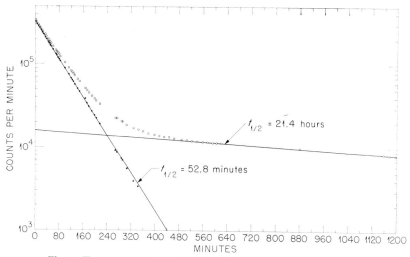

Fig. 1. Two-component decay curve for a mixture of I^{133} and I^{134}.

as a function of time. If all the radiations detected have the same half-life, the decay curve should be a straight line and the $t_{1/2}$ value can be read directly from the plot. If the source contains several independent activities with different half-lives, the analysis is carried out by first subtracting out a straight-line plot for the longest-lived component, and then in succession doing the same for the longest half-life remaining. An example of a complex decay curve is given in Figure 1. It shows a mixture of 52.8-min. I^{134} and 21.4-hr. I^{133}. It was by a careful analysis of this curve that the half-life of I^{134} was determined as 52.8 ± 0.3 min. (114). Considerable use is now being made of electronic computers for the analysis of complex decay curves (e.g., see reference 153).

In the absence of more refined means for identifying the individual members of a mixture of radioactive isotopes (e.g., by pulse-height analysis as described in Section VI.5.F), the analysis of the decay curve in the manner described above can be a valuable tool. If the mixture of activities produces a very complex decay curve, then it is often possible to suppress various components by measuring the decay through different thicknesses of absorbing material.

Half-lives ranging from a few seconds to a few years are conveniently measured with ordinary time-keeping devices. However, for lifetimes of the order of a second or somewhat less, measurement is considerably more difficult and demands development of a specific system for handling the situation. For example, with a rather novel scheme, Campbell and Nelson (37) were able to separate Pb^{207m} from its parent Bi^{207} and measure the half-life of the former as 0.8 sec. They adsorbed Bi^{207} on a strong base quaternary amine polystyrene divinyl benzene resin and pumped, at a known constant rate, $0.5M$ HCl through the resin and into a length of glass tubing. A steady-state distribution of Pb^{207m}, which is not adsorbed by the resin, is established down the tubing, so that by measuring the activity at various distances from the bed they obtained a measure of the Pb^{207m} half-life. Very short half-lives in the range of μsec.–nsec. can be measured by the method of variable-delay coincidences (cf., Section VI.5.G).

Considerable difficulty is also often encountered in measuring extremely long half-lives for which there is very little change in the value of dN/dt over periods of several years. A useful method for handling such cases is to determine the specific activity of the isotope from which the decay constant λ, and hence the half-life, may be obtained. Another method for getting λ is from a determination of dN/dt by calorimetric measurement of the heating effect caused by the emitted radiations. For example, a half-life value of 2.41×10^{14} years (217) has been determined for Pu^{239} by the latter method.

C. GROWTH–DECAY RELATIONSHIPS

Up to this point we have discussed only the relatively simple case of independently decaying activities. However, suppose, for example, that the experimenter is doing an exchange reaction for which the only tracer isotope available decays to a daughter which is also radioactive. Now he is faced with a much more complicated situation, especially if the method of counting the activity does not involve energy analysis. He must determine, at a given time after separation, what fraction of the activity is due to the parent and what to the daughter. A general treatment for handling such decay data is given below.

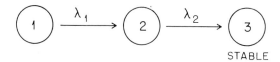

STABLE

Fig. 2. Illustration of chain decay.

Consider the case of radionuclide 1 decaying to 2 decaying to a stable product as illustrated in Figure 2. Now we know that the disintegration rate of 1 is $-dN_1/dt = \lambda_1 N_1$ and that the number of 1 atoms at any given time is $N_1 = N_1{}^0 e^{-\lambda_1 t}$. The second species, 2, is formed at the rate $\lambda_1 N_1$ and itself decays at the rate $\lambda_2 N_2$. Hence,

$$dN_2/dt = \lambda_1 N_1 - \lambda_2 N_2$$

which on substitution becomes

$$dN_2/dt + \lambda_2 N_2 - \lambda_1 N_1{}^0 e^{-\lambda_1 t} = 0 \qquad (6)$$

The solution for this first-order linear differential equation is

$$N_2 = \frac{\lambda_1}{\lambda_2 - \lambda_1} N_1{}^0 (e^{-\lambda_1 t} - e^{-\lambda_2 t}) + N_2{}^0 e^{-\lambda_2 t} \qquad (7)$$

The first group of terms shows the growth of the daughter from parent, and the decay of the daughter atoms. The last term represents the contribution at any time from daughter atoms present initially.

When parent–daughter decay relationships are considered, it is advantageous to consider equation 7 in the light of three general ranges of parent–daughter half-lives. If the parent is longer lived than the daughter ($\lambda_1 < \lambda_2$), ranging from about a factor of 10 up to almost 100, a case of *transient equilibrium* exists. When $\lambda_1 \ll \lambda_2$, that is, the half-life of the parent is about 100 times or greater than that of the daughter, the situation may be classified as a state of *secular equilibrium*. For each of these two cases there will at first appear a growth in the amount of activity which rises to a maximum value and then proceeds to decay exponentially with a half-life characteristic of that of the parent. The third case is that in which the parent is shorter lived than the daughter ($\lambda_1 > \lambda_2$), and the result is that no equilibrium condition can ever be attained. By making a few simple assumptions for each of these three categories, the complexity of equation 7 is reduced considerably. The results obtained may show some deviation from the rigorous treatment, but in most cases they will be satisfactory.

Transient Equilibrium. In the case of transient equilibrium, it can be seen that at any time t the term $e^{-\lambda_2 t}$ of equation 7 is smaller than $e^{-\lambda_1 t}$. Then after t becomes large, $e^{-\lambda_2 t}$ and $N_2^0 e^{-\lambda_2 t}$ are both negligible terms, leaving

$$N_2 = [\lambda_1/(\lambda_2 - \lambda_1)]N_1^0 e^{-\lambda_1 t} \tag{8}$$

In equation 2 we have $N = N_0 e^{-\lambda t}$, which on substituting in equation 8 gives

$$(N_2/N_1) = \lambda_1/(\lambda_2 - \lambda_1) \tag{9}$$

But since the experimental quantity measured in most cases is counting rate, it is helpful to express equation 9 in such terms. We know that $\mathbf{R} = \epsilon\lambda N = \epsilon N_D$, but here, for simplicity, it will be assumed that the radiations from both the parent and daughter are detected with equal efficiency, although in actual practice the appropriate detection efficiencies must be used. Equation 9 then becomes

$$(\mathbf{R}_2/\mathbf{R}_1) = \lambda_2/(\lambda_2 - \lambda_1)$$

or

$$\mathbf{R}_1 = \mathbf{R}_2 [(\lambda_2 - \lambda_1)/\lambda_2] \tag{10}$$

so that at any time t, the counting rate due to the parent is easily determined. The growth–decay curve for a case of transient equilibrium is shown in Figure 3.

Secular Equilibrium. Consider a limiting case of equation 7 for which the half-life of the parent is much larger than that for the daughter (and also greater than the length of any experiment to be performed). For this situation of secular equilibrium where $\lambda_1 \ll \lambda_2$ equation 9 reduces to

$$N_2/N_1 = \lambda_1/\lambda_2$$

i.e.,

$$\lambda_1 N_1 = \lambda_2 N_2 \tag{11}$$

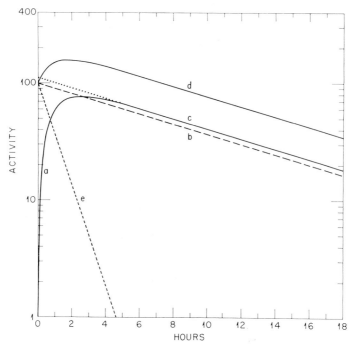

Fig. 3. Illustration of transient equilibrium. a = Growth of daughter activity in an initially pure parent fraction. b = Activity due to parent ($t_{1/2}$ = 6.9 hr.). c = Total daughter activity in state of transient equilibrium. d = Total activity. e = Decay of freshly isolated source of daughter activity ($t_{1/2}$ = 0.69 hr.).

and equation 10 becomes

$$\mathbf{R}_1 = \mathbf{R}_2 \tag{12}$$

Here we see that at equilibrium the parent and daughter disintegration rates are the same. Beyond this point the decay follows the half-life of the parent. Regardless of the value of N_2^0, the same equilibrium value for the disintegration rate is approached. Figure 4 shows an analysis for a growth–decay curve involving secular equilibrium.

A situation of secular equilibrium is commonplace in the production of radioactive species, e.g., production with a steadily operating cyclotron or reactor. For a solution of N_2 as a function of time we use equation 7 and set $N_2^0 = 0$ at $t = 0$, use $e^{-\lambda_1 t} = 1$ since $\lambda_1 \ll \lambda_2$, and in place of $\lambda_1 N_1^0$ substitute a constant, B, which corresponds to the constant rate of production of radioactive nuclei.

$$N_2 = (B/\lambda_2)(1 - e^{-\lambda_2 t}) \tag{13}$$

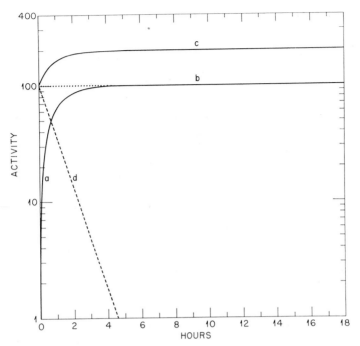

Fig. 4. Illustration of secular equilibrium. a = Growth of daughter activity in an initially pure parent fraction. b = Activity due to parent ($t_{1/2} = \alpha$). This is also the daughter activity in a state of secular equilibrium. c = Total activity. d = Decay of freshly isolated daughter fraction ($t_{1/2} = 0.69$ hr.).

It can be seen that after bombarding the target for a time corresponding to one half-life of the activity of interest, 50% of the maximum attainable yield has been achieved; after two half-lives, 75%; and so on, approaching the maximum limiting value given by B/λ_2.

No Equilibrium. Figure 5 gives the analysis of a parent–daughter decay for a case in which radioactive equilibrium is never attained ($\lambda_1 > \lambda_2$). The source, which is free of daughter atoms at $t = 0$, shows at first a daughter growth which passes through a maximum and then decays with the half-life of the daughter. If $\lambda_1 >> \lambda_2$, then analysis of the two components can be done in the same manner as for two unrelated activities, i.e., the longer-lived component can be extrapolated exponentially back to $t = 0$, and subtracted from the gross curve to give the second component. This approximation is satisfactory since the N_1^0 atoms decay to N_2 atoms so early that one may consider $N_1^0 = N_2^0$. If equal detection efficiencies are assumed again, the ratio of the two half-lives is given by the ratio of

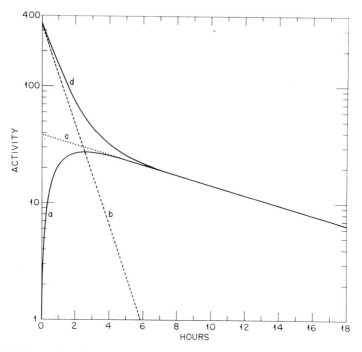

Fig. 5. Illustration of case of no equilibrium. a = Growth of daughter activity in an initially pure parent fraction. b = Activity due to parent ($t_{1/2}$ = 0.69 hr.). c = Final decay curve extrapolated to t = 0. Slope corresponds to $t_{1/2}$ = 6.9 hr. d = Total activity.

the initial parent disintegration rate to the extrapolated value of the daughter rate:

$$\frac{\lambda_1 N_1^0}{\lambda_2 N_1^0} = \frac{\lambda_1}{\lambda_2} = \frac{(t_{1/2})_2}{(t_{1/2})_1} \tag{14}$$

A useful concept in dealing with transient-equilibrium and no-equilibrium cases is the time t_m required for the growth of a daughter to reach a maximum in a freshly separated parent fraction. It can be shown that t_m is given by

$$t_m = [1/(\lambda_2 - \lambda_1)]\ln(\lambda_2/\lambda_1) \tag{15}$$

For secular equilibrium the time t_m is infinite.

Here we have dealt with three general classes of parent-daughter half-lives for which equation 7 is considerably simplified by a few minor assumptions. In all the cases considered it is possible to resolve the decay of the parent and daughter into two straight-line components on semilog paper. There are, however, conditions for which this is not possible. For example, when $\lambda_1 = \lambda_2$, the limiting slope of the decay curve is that of the given half-life, but in an actual measurement, the decay curve will never become a straight line. In fact, any time λ_1 and λ_2 have very similar values, to resolve the decay curves and to determine the half-lives of parent and daughter will be a very difficult task. It will be necessary under these conditions to resort to some method of counting the activities separately, such as by pulse-height analysis, by counting through selected absorbers, by beta-ray spectrometry, or by "milking" the daughter activity at given intervals.

2. Modes of Decay

A. GENERAL CONSIDERATIONS OF UNSTABLE NUCLEI

The prime requirement for the occurrence of any form of nuclear decay is that the mass (energy) of the unstable parent species be greater than that of the daughter species. But before specifically considering the individual types of nuclear decay, let us look at some of the very general features to be observed in an over-all examination of all known nuclides.

A plot of nuclear *binding energy** versus proton number (Z) for an odd mass family of isobars† gives points that form a parabolic curve. If a similar plot is made for an even-mass isobaric family, the points will form two parabolas, the odd neutron–odd proton members lying on a curve just above the neighboring odd-mass parabola, and the even proton–even neutron members lying on another curve immediately below the latter.

Parabolic distributions for the odd mass 125 and the even mass 128 isobars are shown in Figure 6. The energies shown are not experimental, but instead are those calculated (78) from one of the several semiempirical expressions for nuclear binding energies [e.g., see reference 36]. For most of the points, the available experimental data show small deviations from the computed values given in Figure 6; however, by using these semi-empirical values, the general trends for a broader span of Z values can be shown. The binding-energy separation between any pair of isobars is equal to the total energy available for beta decay between the given pair (for a discussion of beta decay see Part C of this section). As is generally found, the odd-A parabola of Figure 6 has one stable species near its minimum and the remaining members of this isobaric family are unstable with respect to beta decay or electron capture. That is, those members on the sides of this parabola decay through the intermediate members of the family until the stable

---

* The binding energy is the energy equivalent of the difference between the measured mass M of a nucleus and the combined masses of its constituent nucleons as independent entities. Any of a number of other parameters which are related to the total binding energy also could be used for this discussion.

† Isobars are nuclides with the same mass number A, but with different atomic numbers, e.g., $_{73}Ta^{184}$, $_{74}W^{184}$, and $_{75}Re^{184}$ are members of the same isobaric family.

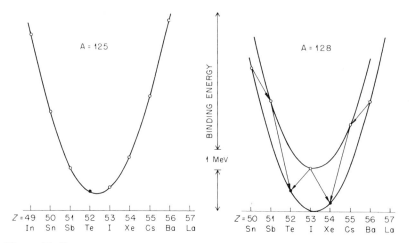

Fig. 6. Binding-energy parabolas for $A = 125$ and $A = 128$. The points on both of these parabolas were calculated from a semiempirical expression. Open circles represent β^- unstable nuclei, the full circles stable nuclei. The energy separation between any two isobars is the total energy available for beta decay between the pair. Note that on the left there is only one stable isobar and on the right there are two, and that both of the latter are on the even-even parabola. These data are taken from reference 78.

product is reached. All members on the odd–odd parabola in Figure 6 are radioactive. From any radioactive member on either the odd–odd or the even–even curve, decay will proceed through the isobaric chain until a stable nuclide is reached on the even–even parabola. There are usually two, as in the case here, and sometimes three possible beta-stable isobars of the even–even type.

When the parabolas for all values of A are displayed in three dimensions, the binding-energy surfaces are obtained. Each of these surfaces has the shape of a valley whose walls are rather steep at the very low mass end. Going to higher masses, there is a general rise in the floor of the valley and the walls take on a much more gentle slope. The three binding-energy surfaces are not only important to understanding the trends in nuclear decay, but are also very useful in predicting the properties of new radioactivities.

In the low- and medium-mass regions, beta decay is the principal mode by which radioactive transformations take place. But in the region of high Z (for the most part $Z > 82$), the energetics are such that additional modes of decay are available. These are by alpha-particle emission and by spontaneous fission.

In general, if a nucleus is left in an excited state following beta decay or heavy-particle emission, it goes to the ground state by the emission of gamma rays. However, there is another, but less probable, mode of decay which can occur when the excitation energy available to a nuclide (on the neutron-rich side of a parabola) is greater than the binding energy of the last neutron for that nucleus. This mode is by emission of *delayed neutrons*. N^{17} is an example of one of these so-called delayed neutron emitters. It decays by beta emission to a level in O^{17} which immediately ejects a neutron that presumably leaves an O^{16} nucleus in its ground state. The steps of the reaction may be written as

$$N^{17} \rightarrow O^{17} + \beta^- \text{ (4.2 sec. half-life)}$$
$$O^{17} \rightarrow O^{16} + n \text{ (instantaneously)}$$

At least hypothetically, on the neutron-deficient side of beta stability, a similar situation exists for *delayed proton* emission.

B. ALPHA DECAY*

With the discovery of alpha, beta, and gamma radiations from radioactive nuclei at about the beginning of the twentieth century, the search for an explanation of nuclear phenomena began. The first tentative steps were aimed toward an understanding of these emitted particles. In 1903, Rutherford was able to deflect radium alpha particles (He^4 nuclei) by electric and magnetic fields and to determine a preliminary e/m value of ~ 6000 e.m.u. In 1909, he and Royds, in a rather ingenious manner, demonstrated that these heavy particles were helium nuclei traveling at very high speeds.

Although alpha-particle emission is observed in a few rare-earth nuclides, this mode of decay is restricted primarily to the heaviest nuclei. To understand this, let us consider the building up of heavier nuclei by the process of adding neutrons and protons to lighter ones. As the number of protons increases, the Coulombic repulsion does likewise, and thus the energy that binds the nucleus together is effectively diminished (the Coulomb repulsion increases with Z^2, while the total binding energy increases approximately as A). Beyond a certain point the driving force toward losing positive charge finally results in the appearance of alpha radioactivity.

It was in 1928 that G. Gamow and, independently, R. W. Gurney and E. U. Condon presented satisfactory quantum-mechanical explanations for alpha-particle emission. Basically, their proposed *one-body model* assumes that the alpha particle is preformed inside the nucleus. The nuclear potential is assumed to be a square well out to the nuclear radius and beyond that point it has the form of a pure Coulomb repulsion. A typical potential energy diagram is shown schematically in Figure 7. As indicated,

---

* There are many excellent reviews on this subject: for example, see references 97, 178, and 179.

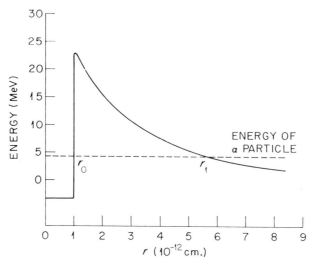

Fig. 7. Typical schematic diagram showing the potential energy of an alpha-particle daughter–nucleus system as a function of r, the distance between their centers. The radius r_0 is the sum of the radii of the residual nucleus and the alpha particle, and within this region strong attractive nuclear forces exist. Between the radii r_0 and r_1, the interaction of the two particles is purely electrostatic and beyond r_1 the two particles emerge as independent systems.

the wave function representing the alpha particle does not go to zero at the wall of this potential barrier. Instead it has a small but finite value beyond, and it is by the process of "tunneling" through the barrier that emission of these heavy charged particles is assumed to proceed. And as a consequence, alpha particles of only a few MeV energy are able to get over (through) a potential barrier which is much higher.

But there remains the question of why alpha particles are emitted preferentially to other heavy particles such as protons, He^3 nuclei, etc. The answer is that, energywise, this is the most economical process. This fact is illustrated in Table I. Here we show in the manner given by Halliday (96) the calculated kinetic energy releases for various modes of heavy-particle decay of U^{232}. Only in the case of alpha emission is there a positive kinetic energy release; hence, this is the only mode listed that occurs spontaneously for U^{232}. The alpha particle is a very stable entity as a result of its unusually large binding energy, i.e., its mass is much less than the combined masses of two free protons and two free neutrons. In fact, the proton in an alpha particle "weighs" about 7 MeV less than it does as an individual entity.

From a binding energy standpoint, it might be expected that larger aggregates of nucleons consisting of multiples of alpha particles, such as

O^{16}, should be emitted with an even greater probability than are alpha particles. The coalescing of four alpha particles into an O^{16} nucleus would result in an additional 15 MeV of stabilization. However, this additional 15 MeV available for decay by emission of an O^{16} nucleus is not sufficient to offset the large increase in the Coulomb barrier to a particle with eight units of charge. As a consequence, the emission of large O^{16} particles is less probable than alpha-particle emission by many orders of magnitude.

TABLE I
KINETIC ENERGY RELEASE FOR VARIOUS MODES OF DECAY OF U^{232}
(Computed from known masses)

Emitted particle	Kinetic-energy release, MeV	Emitted particle	Kinetic-energy release, MeV
n	− 7.15	He^4	+5.38
H^1	− 6.05	He^5	−2.28
H^2	−10.5	He^6	−5.82
H^3	−10.1	Li^6	−3.78
He^3	− 9.6	Li^7	−1.83

From Figure 7 it follows that the higher in the potential well a nucleus may lie, the thinner the Coulomb barrier at that point, and hence, the more probable is barrier penetration, resulting in a shorter lifetime and a greater decay energy for the alpha emitter. The connection between decay energy and lifetime for alpha emission is demonstrated in the case of Th^{232} which emits 4-MeV alpha particles with a half-life of $\sim 10^{10}$ years and Th^{224} with corresponding values of 7.1 MeV and about 1 sec. Much use has been made of the energy–lifetime relationship to predict the half-lives of new alpha emitters, e.g., see references 178 and 179.

For some of the heaviest nuclei we find that if they are split roughly in two, the combined masses of these two resulting components is less than the mass of the original nucleus. This condition gives rise to another mode of decay, *spontaneous fission*. Obviously, the potential barrier to nuclear fission is much higher than the barrier to alpha decay and, hence, the number of nuclides that fission spontaneously is expected to be quite small. However, for some of the heavy stable nuclei, an excitation of the nucleus by only a few million electron volts takes the system over the barrier and fission follows within a very small fraction of a second. The fission process not only produces two lighter nuclei of similar masses, but also is accompanied by the emission of neutrons and by a very large energy release, close to 200 MeV. Further discussion on the fission process is included in Section IV.2.A.

C. BETA DECAY AND ASSOCIATED PHENOMENA

The process of beta decay represents transitions between neighboring isobars; stated differently, it is a nuclear transition in which the nuclear charge changes by ± 1, but the number of nucleons in the nucleus remains constant. In the case of β^- decay, a neutron transforms into a proton by the emission of a negative electron (negatron), and in β^+ a proton transforms into a neutron by the emission of a positive electron (positron). As electrons do not exist as individual entities within the nucleus, they must be created in the beta-decay event. The process is analogous to the creation of photons in gamma-ray emission which will be discussed in Part D of this section. An alternative and competing mode of decay to positron emission is the capture of an orbital electron. The known lifetimes of beta-decay processes range from about 10^{-2} sec. up to 10^{11} years.

A summary of the conditions describing the instability of a nucleus to beta decay follows:

$$\beta^- \text{ decay:} \qquad M_{A,Z} > M_{A,(Z+1)} \tag{16}$$

$$\beta^+ \text{ decay:} \qquad M_{A,Z} > M_{A,(Z-1)} + 2m_0 \tag{17}$$

$$\text{electron capture:} \qquad M_{A,Z} > M_{A,(Z-1)} \tag{18}$$

where M is the atomic mass of a given nuclide; A,Z identifies the parent nuclide with respect to its mass number A and nuclear charge Z; $A,(Z+1)$ and $A,(Z-1)$ identify the daughter products; and m_0 is the mass of an electron.

The role of chemistry has been an important one in the history of understanding beta decay. A change in atomic number can be identified directly if the daughter nuclide formed is also radioactive. From the chemical properties of successive members of natural radioactivities, Soddy was able to recognize the nature of the beta-decay process. Even if the daughter is not radioactive, it can be identified by mass spectrometric means, provided a sufflcien tnumber of atoms is present.

Dirac Theory of Positive and Negative Electrons. Much of our theoretical concept of the positron stems from the early work of Dirac. The existence of negative electrons had been recognized for some time when Dirac, on the basis of his relativistic quantum theory of the electron, said there should be electron states with energies larger than m_0c^2, the rest energy of an electron, but with either positive or negative signs. He suggested that an electron could be raised from a negative to a positive energy state by adding at least $2m_0c^2$ (1.02 MeV) of energy, which would result in the appearance of an electron and a hole in a negative "sea" of electrons, the hole having the properties of a positively charged electron. The first verification of Dirac's theory came with the discovery of positrons in cosmic rays. From this concept of Dirac, it follows that if an isobar on the neutron-deficient side of a binding-energy parabola does not lie at least $2m_0c^2$ away from the nuclide to which it decays, then a positron cannot be emitted and decay can proceed only by capture of an orbital electron.

When the positron from β^+ decay has come almost to rest from interactions with matter, positron–electron annihilation occurs. This process, which accounts for the very short lifetime of positrons, may be pictured as the filling of the hole in the negative sea by one of the many electrons which are available in matter. The energy available as a result of annihilating an electron and a positron is almost always released in the form of two gamma quanta, each with an energy of 0.51 MeV. These photons are emitted at 180° to each other, but nevertheless randomly with respect to the original positron direction.

Beta-Ray Spectral Distributions. For many years the observed shapes of beta-ray spectra presented a very puzzling problem. It was well known from studies of alpha- and gamma-ray spectra that nuclei existed in discrete energy states. Yet, unlike alpha- and gamma-ray transitions, in all cases the beta decay between a discrete state in one nucleus and a discrete level in the daughter nucleus gave a continuous distribution of beta-ray kinetic energies varying from zero to a maximum which is called the *end-point* energy. This situation is demonstrated in Figure 8a which shows a beta spectrum of P^{32}, a 14.5-day activity with a single beta-ray group having an end-point energy of 1.71 MeV.

The continuous energy distribution in beta-ray spectra seemed to violate the well-established laws of conservation of energy and momentum. An additional complication was that the laws concerning angular momentum seemed to be violated in the beta-decay process. At that time, the concept that parity, too, should be conserved in beta decay also posed a problem. In order to explain what appeared to be anomalous behavior in beta decay, Pauli, in 1930, suggested that the emission of a beta particle is accompanied by the emission of a light neutral particle called the neutrino (ν). The neutrino (Italian for the small neutral one) was assumed to have a negligible rest mass, zero charge, an intrinsic spin angular momentum of $1/2\ \hbar$, and negative parity.

The probability for the interaction of a neutrino with matter is so extremely small that it escaped direct detection for many years. Only recently was direct proof for existence of this elusive particle shown. This was by Reines and Cowan (191) with an experiment in which they observed a series of events triggered by an initial interaction of neutrinos with protons to form a neutron and a positron. The interaction cross section was found to be about 10^{-44} cm.^{2}, in agreement with theoretical expectations.

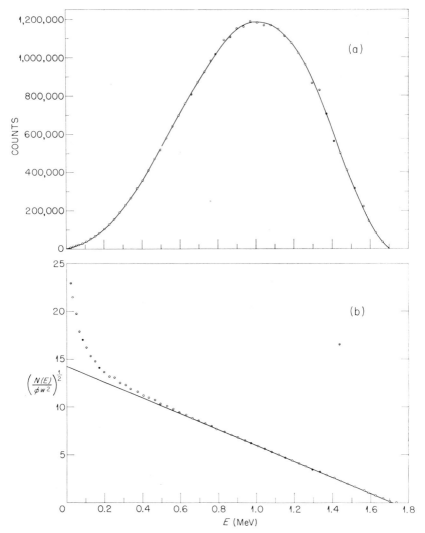

Fig. 8. (a) Energy distribution of P^{32} beta rays taken with a magnetic spectrometer. (b) Fermi plot of P^{32} beta spectrum. The ordinate scale is in arbitrary units proportional to $P(W)/[F(\pm Z,W)W(W^2 - 1)^{1/2}]^{1/2}$. The deviation from a straight line below about 600 k.e.v. is due mainly to scattering. The sharp upturn in the distribution at low energy is due to the presence of a small amount of P^{33} which has beta rays with a maximum energy of 250 keV (data from Ketelle and Brosi, reference 124).

Fermi Theory of Beta Decay.

In 1934, E. Fermi presented a theory of beta decay based heavily on the earlier neutrino hypothesis of Pauli. The success of Fermi's theory, which is somewhat analogous to the theory of emission of radiation from atoms, was the first strong proof of Pauli's hypothesis. In this theory of beta decay it is possible to predict scalar quantities such as the shape of the beta spectrum and the half-life of the beta emitter in relation to the maximum energy W_0, the atomic number Z, and the change in nuclear spin ΔI. For transitions with $\Delta I = 0$ or 1, the probability for beta particles with energies between W and $W + dW$ is

$$P(W)dW = K \times M_{if}^2 \times F(\pm Z, W)W(W^2 - 1)^{1/2}(W_0 - W)^2 dW \quad (19)$$

Involved in the first term, K, on the right side of equation 19 are a number of universal constants as well as one applicable strictly to beta decay; M_{if} is the so-called transition matrix element that depends on the form of interaction involved. The square of the matrix element can be interpreted physically as the degree of overlap of the nucleon wave functions for the initial and final states. In the last group of terms W is the total energy of the electron (kinetic energy plus the rest mass) in units of m_0c^2; W_0 is the maximum possible value of W; and the function $F(\pm Z, W)$ is a measure of the effect of the Coulomb barrier on the energy distribution.

In cases where $\Delta I > 1$, the distribution is complicated by additional terms. For these cases, the electron and neutrino must carry away orbital angular momentum, which imposes another restraint on the process. The result is that both the low- and high-energy ends of the beta distribution are altered. Further deviations of the beta spectrum from the predicted distribution of equation 19 may be caused by artifacts such as scattering of the electrons or the superposition of conversion electrons.

In recent years Fermi's original theory has met its most severe test as the understanding of beta decay has undergone an amazing revolution. It all began in 1956 with a startling hypothesis, advanced by Lee and Yang (138), that parity was not conserved in "weak interactions,"* of which beta decay is a prime example. Their proposal that nature makes a distinction between right and left handedness in producing the "weak decay" interactions has led to a series of brilliant experiments and the results of these experiments have confirmed the ideas of Lee and Yang.

Despite this upheaval in the concepts of the beta-decay process, the theoretical formulation is still essentially that of Fermi. As pointed out above, in classical beta-decay experiments, such as in a determination of spectral shapes, scalar quantities are measured and they are definitely invariant with respect to space inversion; hence, the Fermi theory is unaltered for such considerations. The necessary modifications to the original formulation appear mainly as small-order effects in the nuclear coupling constants and are manifest only in beta-decay experiments that give in-

* The magnitude of a weak interaction is intermediary between a "very weak interaction" such as gravitational force and a "strong interaction" such as Coulombic forces.

formation about pseudoscalar quantities, e.g., angular distributions of beta rays from oriented nuclei.

Determination of Maximum Beta-Ray Energy. Accurate determinations of the maximum beta energy from the beta spectrum is extremely difficult as evidenced in Figure 8a. This problem is alleviated by rearranging equation 19 and making a plot of $\{P(W)/[F(\pm Z,W)W(W^2 - 1)^{1/2}]\}^{1/2}$ against W or kinetic energy E. Such a representation, known as a *Fermi plot* or *Kurie plot*, is usually a straight line, intercepting the energy axis at W_0. The beta-ray end-point energy of P^{32} is easily read from the Fermi plot of Figure 8b. Here, the deviation from a straight line at about 700 keV results mainly from scattering, although there is present a small amount of P^{33}, which emits beta rays with a maximum energy of 250 keV.

In cases where there are two or three beta rays in a spectrum, a Fermi analysis, is, indeed, most valuable. The components may be analyzed in a fashion similar to that employed for decay curves. The process involves first an extrapolation of the most energetic beta-ray component in the Fermi plot back to zero energy. This component is converted back to a beta-ray distribution of the type shown in Figure 8a. Then this distribution is subtracted from the gross distribution, a Fermi plot is made of the difference, and once again the procedure is repeated on the most energetic component that remains. This process can, in principle, be repeated for many beta components. In practice, however, it is usually found that after about three components are accounted for, further analysis is of little value, due to compounded errors. This analysis gives both end-point energies and relative intensities for the beta-ray groups. To get the relative intensity of each component, it is necessary to take the area under its energy distribution.

Electron Capture. As pointed out above, the capture of an orbital electron by the nucleus is a process that competes with positron decay, and in the cases where the total decay energy available is less than 1.02 MeV ($2m_0c^2$), only electron capture occurs. Since the same selection rules apply to electron capture as to the competing positron decay to any particular level, it is possible to predict the ratio of the number of nuclei transformed by these two processes. Experimental measurements of the electron capture to positron ratio are in general agreement with the theory.

The probability for electron capture is greatest in the K shell since quantum-mechanically these electrons have the largest wave function amplitudes at the nucleus. It follows that electron-capture probability is greater for high-Z nuclides, since the electron orbits are smaller and, therefore, the chance for an electron to be within the nuclear volume is greater. Also favoring an increase in the electron capture to positron ratio with increasing Z is the fact that the potential barrier to positron emission increases with Z. These two factors account for the absence of positron emitters among the heaviest elements. There is a finite probability of capturing L, M etc. electrons also, and in fact one way of determining the total decay energy in electron capture is from a measurement of the L- to K-capture ratio (92). Similar to β^- and β^+ decay, electron capture is accompanied by the emission of neutrinos. There is one distinct difference, however. The electrons are captured from discrete energy states, and therefore the neutrinos emitted are monoenergetic.

*Auger Electrons.** Following electron capture, an electron from a higher shell will fill the vacancy. This results in either the emission of an x ray whose energy corresponds to the difference in binding energies of the electrons in the two shells involved, or in the emission of an electron from a higher shell. The latter of these is known as the *Auger process*. The vacancies left by either process can likewise be filled, etc., so that for any electron-capturing nuclide there will appear a spectrum of x rays and/or Auger electrons characteristic of the nucleus $(Z - 1)$.

The Auger process has been shown to arise primarily from an interaction between two electrons; one of the electrons fills the vacancy in an inner shell and the other is ejected from the atom. However, a small fraction (of the order of magnitude $e^2/\hbar c$) is the result of a true internal absorption of an x ray in which the x ray strikes and ejects an outer electron. In either case the kinetic energy, E_e, of the Auger electron is approximately

$$E_e = E_K - 2E_L \tag{20}$$

where E_K and E_L are the binding energies of the K and L electrons, respectively. Detection of these electrons is even more difficult than detection of the x rays following electron capture. The proportional counter and the magnetic spectrometer have proven to be excellent means for obtaining the spectra of Auger electrons. Here the very thinnest windows must be used in the detection apparatus.

The fraction of vacancies in a given shell that are filled with accompanying x-ray emission is called the *fluorescence yield* and the fraction that is filled with accompanying Auger processes is the *Auger yield*. The probability is nearly unity that an x ray will be emitted in high-Z elements and approaches zero for low-Z elements.

Bremsstrahlung. Following electron capture or any process that creates a vacancy in an inner electron shell, the acceleration of the electron toward its own nuclear field results in the emission of *inner bremsstrahlung*. This is a continuous distribution of very low-energy gamma rays ranging in energy from zero up to the total kinetic energy of the accelerating electron.

* For a comprehensive treatment of the subject see Burhop (33).

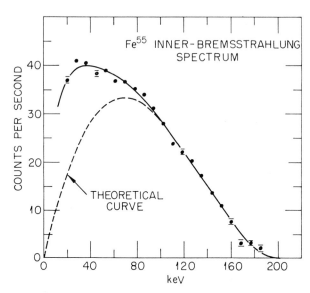

Fig. 9. "Inner-bremsstrahlung" spectrum of Fe[55]. An end-point energy of 206 keV represents the total energy separation between the ground states of Fe[55] and its daughter Mn[55] (data from reference 9).

The theory for this process following K capture has been worked out by Morrison and Schiff (157). One important case for which the theory has been experimentally confirmed is with Fe[55] (reference 26). This nuclide, which has considerable importance as a tracer, decays solely by electron capture, and it is by its low-energy x-ray and inner-bremsstrahlung spectra that detection is made possible. Figure 9 shows the continuous distribution of gamma rays of Fe[55] taken from the data of Bell et al. (9). The upper energy portion of the spectrum is in good agreement with theoretical predictions. An end-point energy of 206 keV represents the total energy separation between the ground states of Fe[55] and its daughter Mn[55].

Whereas inner bremsstrahlung is emitted in electron-capture processes, the same type of radiation from the interaction of a beta particle with the field of its own nucleus is referred to as *internal bremsstrahlung*. This internal bremsstrahlung is usually masked by the beta spectrum and by a third class of "slowing-down radiation," *external bremsstrahlung*. This latter radiation is that produced by the deceleration of the beta particle, either by the electrostatic fields of other nuclei in the source or by those of some absorbing material external to the source.

Bremsstrahlung radiation is not restricted to electron-capture processes. When any accelerating charged particle interacts with an electric or magnetic field, it will radiate low-energy photons. However, the probability of

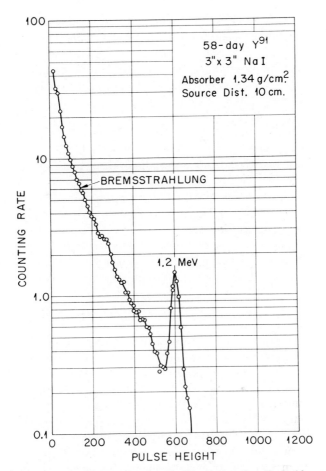

Fig. 10. Gamma-ray spectrum of 58-day Y[91] illustrating the effect of bremsstrahlung from a source in which the beta/gamma intensity ratio is very large (data taken from reference 104).

bremsstrahlung emission decreases with the square of the mass of the incident charged particle. Alpha particles, for example, will produce approximately 10^{-6} the bremsstrahlung of an electron with the same velocity.

Although in the cases where electron capture is the only mode of decay the presence of bremsstrahlung is indeed most helpful as a means of detection, in other cases it may prove a considerable difficulty. For example, suppose the experimenter wishes to do a pulse-height analysis of the gamma spectrum of 58-day Y[91] shown in Figure 10. Only 0.2% of the beta decay of this activity feeds a level in Zr[91] at 1.19 MeV with the remainder of the beta rays going to the ground state (end-point energy of this group is 1.55

MeV). Since the gamma-ray spectrum is almost completely dominated by the bremsstrahlung background, a reliable determination of the gamma-ray intensity is difficult, to say the least. One important consideration toward reducing bremsstrahlung background is to use materials only of low Z around the source and detector, as the probability of bremsstrahlung production increases with Z^2 of the absorber.

D. GAMMA RADIATION AND ASSOCIATED PROCESSES

Gamma Transitions. When a nucleus is excited, but with insufficient energy to permit particle emission, it usually returns to its normal or ground state by emission of electromagnetic radiation. Gamma radiation, discovered by Villard (225) in 1900, differs from ordinary light only in that its wavelength is much shorter or, correspondingly, its quantum energy much larger.

The packet of gamma radiation sent out as a result of a single transition is termed a *photon*. As a result of Einstein's corpuscular notion of light and the quantum ideas of Planck and de Broglie, the energy, E, of this photon may be written as

$$E = h(c/\lambda) = h\nu = mc^2 (\text{ergs}) \tag{21}$$

where h is Planck's constant, c is the speed of light, λ and ν are the wavelength and frequency, respectively, of the radiation, and m is the equivalent mass. Gamma-ray energies range from as low as a few thousand electron volts up to as high as 8.87 MeV, the latter originating from an excited level of the same energy in O^{16}. In this respect it should be pointed out that gamma rays and x rays, both of which are described by equation 21, are not distinguished from each other on the basis of energies. They are identical in nature and differ in that gamma rays are nuclear in origin while x rays result from electronic rearrangements following any process that creates a vacancy in an inner electron orbital.

Between the highest excited state and the ground state of a nucleus there may exist many intermediate energy levels. Then, if the nucleus exists in a highly excited state, either as a result of alpha or beta decay, or of any other process, a spectrum of gamma rays may be obtained due to de-excitation stepwise down through many of the energy levels. It is true, just as in optical spectroscopy, that selection rules strongly govern the permissible steps for the de-excitation process, and hence the gamma rays emitted. The gamma-ray energy resulting from a transition between two excited nuclear levels is $E_\gamma = \Delta E$, assuming the initial nucleus at rest and neglecting the nuclear recoil energy. Nuclear recoil, which is necessary for momentum conservation, reduces the gamma-ray energy by a small amount, but this is negligible except in certain resonance experiments in which it is necessary to compensate for this recoil loss. It has been recently observed by Mössbauer (158), however, that gamma-ray absorption and emission in certain favored cases can take place without recoil. In these cases it is possible to measure hyperfine splittings of gamma-ray lines caused by effective magnetic fields acting on the magnetic moment of the nucleus.

Internal Conversion. A process that often accompanies, and sometimes even replaces, gamma-ray emission is the emission of internal-conversion electrons. In the process, the energy available for the transition is transferred to an extranuclear electron in the atomic "cortège." Neglecting recoil, the electron is emitted with a kinetic energy equivalent to the gamma-ray transition energy minus the binding energy of the electron. For a given transition, the ratio of the number of conversion electrons to the number of gamma rays emitted is known as the *internal-conversion coefficient, α*. Provided the energy of the gamma transition is sufficient, conversion can occur in any of the electron shells. With a spectrograph of sufficient resolution it is possible to obtain the line spectrum for the conversion electrons, and the differences in energy between the lines may serve to identify the Z and to classify groups of lines resulting from different gamma transitions. From the relative intensities of K, L, M, etc., lines of a given transition, the *multipole order* of the transition and, in turn, the spins of the states involved can be obtained. Tables of theoretical conversion coefficients have been computed by Rose (197) and Sliv and Band (208).

Following internal conversion, the vacancy created in an electron shell will be filled by electrons from higher shells. The processes that follow are very similar to those that follow electron capture, *viz.*, the emission of x rays, Auger electrons, and bremsstrahlung.

Internal Pair Production. There is still another process competing with gamma emission for the de-excitation of a nucleus. This is by production of a positron–electron pair with a threshold of 1.02 MeV $(2m_0c^2)$, the energy equivalent of two electron masses. The difference between the available transition energy and the 1.02-MeV threshold is carried away as kinetic energy by the two particles. An example of this rather uncommon mode of decay occurs with the first excited state of O^{16}. It has an energy of 6.05 MeV and the half-life for the pair-production process in this case is 7×10^{-11} sec. When the positron is annihilated, the 1.02 MeV is recovered in the form of two 0.51-MeV quanta emitted in opposite directions.

Nuclear Isomerism. Any excited nuclear state having a measurable half-life is called an *isomer*. The ground state of the nucleus and its metastable excited state are referred to as an *isomeric pair* and the transition between them as an *isomeric transition*. The lifetime of a gamma transition between two states depends very strongly on spin change. For small spin

change ($\Delta J \leq 2$, where J is total angular momentum of the level) the lifetimes for the transitions range from 10^{-17} to 10^{-10} sec. For a large spin
change such as $\Delta J = 4$ and a low-energy gamma ray of about 100 keV,
the lifetime may be as long as several years. One example of a nuclide
that exhibits isomeric behavior is Zr^{89}. It has a 4.4-min. level at 588 keV
and its ground state decays with a 79-hr. half-life.

Nuclear isomers are not to be confused with the term *isomer* as it occurs
in various other branches of chemistry. The term *isomer* is commonplace
in chemistry for a molecule whose component atoms may be differently
arranged and thus display different properties.

3. Nuclear Decay Schemes

Much use is made of decay schemes (disintegration schemes) to convey
in a concise manner many of the characteristics of nuclides. A decay scheme
is a diagram that shows the modes of decay of the nuclide, their energies
and abundances, the sequence in which the radiations are emitted, the
measurable half-lives of any states, and the spins (total angular momentum)
and parities of the energy levels. In these diagrams, vertical displacements
represent energy, arrows to the right generally indicate a gain in positive

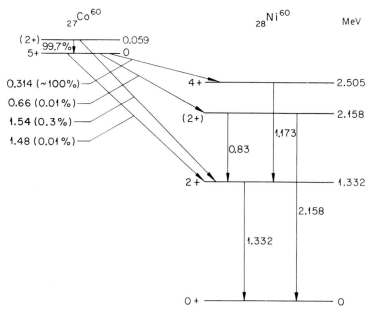

Fig. 11. Decay scheme of Co^{60}. All energies are in MeV. The spin and parity is listed
at the left of each energy level; those values in parentheses are assigned with less certainty
than those without.

charge (β^- decay), and arrows to the left indicate a loss of positive charge (β^+ decay, electron capture, or alpha decay).

For illustrative purposes, the decay scheme of Co^{60} is shown in Figure 11. The 10-min. isomeric state at 0.059 MeV decays primarily to the ground state of Co^{60}, but there is a small beta-ray branch of less than 1% that goes to the 1.332-MeV level in the daughter nucleus, Ni^{60}. Almost all of the ground-state decay of Co^{60} is by emission of a 314-keV beta ray to the 2.505-MeV level in Ni^{60}; very small beta-ray branches are reported to decay to the 2.158- and 1.332-MeV levels.

The two gamma rays of 1.332 and 1.173 MeV are in coincidence; that is, they are emitted in the same decay event. The separation in time between their emission is, in this case, quite short ($<10^{-11}$ sec.); thus, they would appear as simultaneous radiations in the fastest coincidence devices. (For a discussion of coincidence techniques, see Section VI.5.G.) Such coincident gamma rays are often referred to as forming a "cascade." The "crossover transition" for these two gamma rays has not been observed. The term *crossover* refers to a gamma ray that originates at the same level as the upper gamma ray of this coincident pair and terminates at the same level as the lower member of the pair, and in so doing "crosses over" or by-passes the intermediate level, in this case at 1.332 MeV. The crossover transition from the 2.158-MeV level to the ground state has been reported to be present in very low abundance.

It is easy to establish that the 0.314-MeV beta ray goes to the excited level at 2.505 MeV by measuring the beta spectra in coincidence with the 1.332- and 1.173-MeV gamma rays, or by using an arrangement to sum the 1.332- and 1.173-MeV gamma rays and measuring the beta spectrum coincident with this sum.

At the left of each energy level are listed the spin and parity of that state. The values within parentheses are assigned with less certainty than those without.

Strominger, Hollander, and Seaborg (218) have compiled a list of decay schemes utilizing the available information as of February 1958; but for an up-to-date source of such information, the Nuclear Data Sheets (230) should be consulted.

III. INTERACTION OF RADIATIONS WITH MATTER

It is only by interacting with matter that electrons, protons, alpha particles, gamma rays, etc. can be detected. To refer to a good detector for a certain type of radiation is to indicate that the interaction between the two is sufficient to provide an adequate description of the radiation. In order to understand the many types of detection systems and associated instrumentation used in the measurement and characterization of radiation, it is, therefore, important to know something about the way the radiation interacts with matter.

When either charged particles or electromagnetic radiation pass through matter, it is generally true that the main source of energy loss comes from their interaction with electrons. In the case of charged particles, this is easily seen from the fact that heavy charged particles (protons, alpha particles, tritons, etc.) are scattered very little in the interactions which slow them down, whereas incident electrons are deflected to a much greater extent as they interact with matter and lose energy. Energy loss resulting from collisions with nuclei is in general smaller by orders of magnitude. Such is not the case for neutrons, however, as they interact almost totally with the nuclei of atoms. A comprehensive treatment of this latter subject, which will be given no further attention here, is given by Hughes (111).

1. Alpha Particles

The remarks to be made in this section have general applications to the interactions of any heavy charged particle with matter. However, we will limit our discussion mainly to a consideration of alpha radiation since this is usually of most interest to the chemist. For the reader interested in a more thorough coverage of the subject than is given here, a number of excellent references are available (e.g., 1, 12, 23, 65, 222, 231).

A. RANGE

If the alpha particles from a monoenergetic source are counted in air, the disintegration rate appears to remain constant up to a certain distance R (range) from the source, and then somewhat abruptly goes to zero. Ranges of alpha particles are generally determined by absorption methods. For solid absorbers this simply involves inserting different thicknesses of absorber between the alpha source and detector in an evacuated container. The ranges in gases may be obtained by either varying the source-to-detector distance in an environment of the given gas at constant pressure or by leaving the geometry constant and varying the gas pressure.

Figure 12a shows the number of alpha particles observed as a function of the absorber thickness for a monoenergetic source. There is a certain statistical nature associated with the stopping processes as evidenced by the behavior near the end of the range. This effect, referred to as "straggling," is much smaller than that observed in the range curves for electrons to be discussed later. The mean range $\bar{R}$ is defined as the distance at which the integral range curve (a) falls to $1/2$. The point at which the tangent to the curve at the $1/2$ height strikes the x axis is the extrapolated range

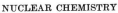

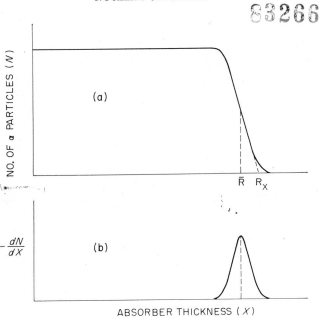

Fig. 12. (*a*) Integral range distribution curve showing the number of alpha particles as a function of absorber thickness. $\bar{R}$ is the mean range and R_x the extrapolated range. (*b*) Differential range distribution.

R_x. The mean range $\bar{R}$ is the form most often used in range tables and in range–energy relations.

If curve (a) of Figure 12 is differentiated, an approximately Gaussian distribution is obtained as shown in curve (b). This is called the differential range distribution and the plot of $-dN/dx$ shows a maximum at the mean range $\bar{R}$.

In Figure 13 the range of alpha particles in air (expressed as mg./cm.²) is shown as a function of energy. Often the range is expressed in terms of the length of absorption path in centimeters. To convert from milligrams per square centimeter to centimeters of air at 15°C. and 760 mm. pressure it is necessary to divide the former by 1.226, the density of air at these standard conditions. A comprehensive collection of charged-particle, range–energy data is given by Whaling (231) and an excellent bibliography of such information has been provided by Brown and Jarmie (30).

Often there arises a need for charged-particle range–energy information in materials for which no data has been accumulated. To carry out the necessary computations for conversion from one type of absorber to another is very time-consuming, as the calculation involves a complicated expression of Z, A, and E, the energy of the charged particle. There are, however, very

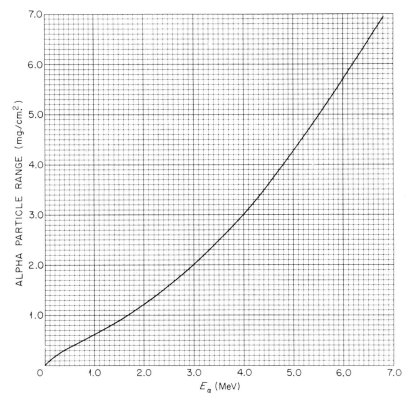

Fig. 13. Mean range of alpha particles in air. Data from reference 12.

simple approximations of this function which give sufficiently accurate results to be useful in many cases. The following expression, taken from reference 78, is applicable for absorbers with $Z > 10$, and can be used for protons, deuterons, and alpha particles with energies between 0.1 and 1000 MeV:

$$(R_Z/R_a) = 0.90 + 0.0275\ Z + (0.06 - 0.0086\ Z)\ \log\ (E/M) \quad (22)$$

R_Z is the range of the particle in element Z in milligrams per square centimeter and R_a its range in air, M is the mass number of the charged particle, and E is the initial energy of the particle in millions of electron volts.

B. ENERGY LOSS

When protons, alpha particles, or any other heavy charged particles interact with electrons, they lose most of their energy by inelastic scattering processes, resulting in ionization and excitation of the atoms in the absorber.

For most cases, elastic and inelastic collisions with the nuclei of the absorbing material and elastic collisions with its atomic electrons contribute only a small part to the energy loss of the incoming alpha particle. The term *scattering* indicates that the incident particles are the same as the outgoing particles. The *elastic* process is one in which kinetic energy is conserved and in *inelastic* scattering, kinetic energy is lost, i.e., the sum of the kinetic energies of the incident particles is greater than that for the outgoing particles, usually as a result of ionization or excitation.

The problem of energy loss was at first treated classically by Bohr (23) and later on, a more accurate quantum-mechanical calculation was done by Bethe (11). From the theory it is predicted that the energy loss dE/dx (where E is the energy of the charged particle and x is the distance traversed in the absorber) depends only on the velocity and the charge and not on the mass of the moving ion, a fact confirmed by experimental observations.

It has been adequately demonstrated that the mechanism of energy loss by charged particles is a manyfold process. Henderson (106), Rutherford (199), Briggs (28), Kapitza (119), and others have shown that when an alpha particle passes through an electron cloud, it will capture one or two electrons and become singly ionized or a helium atom. But after this capture re-ionization occurs quickly through collision with other atoms. For a 1-MeV alpha particle, of the order of 10^3 such exchanges occur along its path, with most of the processes occurring in the last few per cent of its range. It is found both experimentally and theoretically that as long as the alpha-particle velocity is large compared with the Bohr orbital velocity for its K electrons (corresponding to an alpha-particle energy >2 MeV), loss of an electron is much more probable than an electron "pickup" process. Accordingly, the rapid diminishing of the charge on an incoming helium ion occurs shortly before it comes to rest.

In the course of one of these Coulombic collisions there may be considerable kinetic energy transferred from the incoming ion to the electron, resulting in the ejection of the electron from the atom. The electron and ionized atom constitute a primary ion pair. These ejected electrons, called *delta rays*, usually have of the order of 100–200 eV imparted to them by an alpha particle, but in some cases the value may extend to over 1 keV. As the delta ray comes to rest it produces secondary ionization, and in fact about 60–80% of the ionization produced in the absorbing materials by alpha particles results from this secondary effect. It should be pointed out that the theory of stopping of charged particles by matter deals with the loss of their kinetic energy and not with the ionization produced in the absorbing medium. The number of ion pairs formed in the absorber is rather involved with its nature and purity and our knowledge in this area is mostly empirical.

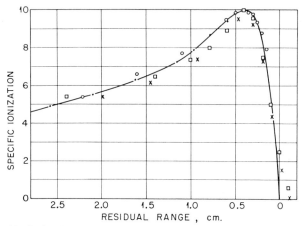

Fig. 14. Specific ionization of an alpha particle as a function of its residual range [data from Holloway and Livingston, *Phys. Rev.*, **54**, 29 (1938)].

Because of their short ranges, it is a simple matter to cause alpha particles to dissipate their energy inside an ionization chamber. The electric current collected is equal to the electronic charge times the number of ion pairs, and in air from 2000–6000 of these ion pairs per millimeter of path may be produced by an alpha particle. The number of ion pairs per unit path length is called the *specific ionization*, $d\mathcal{I}/dx$. Experiments show that an alpha particle must dissipate about 35 eV for each ion pair formed. For alpha particles with energies greater than 1 MeV, the maximum specific ionization occurs about 3 mm. from the end of its range, corresponding to an energy of about 0.37 MeV and a velocity of 4.2×10^8 cm./sec. As the particle moves on toward the end of its range and the energy is further reduced, the specific ionization rapidly falls to zero. This behavior is illustrated in Figure 14 in which the ionization from a single alpha particle as it is slowed down in a gas is plotted against the residual range. Such a plot is commonly called a "Bragg curve."

2. Beta Particles

A. ENERGY LOSS

The ways in which electrons interact with matter and lose energy are qualitatively similar to the mechanisms for heavy charged particle energy loss. That is, electrons below about 1 MeV lose their energy primarily through inelastic collisions with the atomic electrons of the absorbing material resulting in excitation and ionization. The average energy loss per ion pair formed in air by either of the two types of particles is, in fact, about the same ($\sim$35 eV). In reality, however, the mechanisms of energy loss for light and heavy charged particles are quite different, mainly as a result of the very small mass of the electron. Whereas a heavy charged particle suffers very little change in its initial direction following an impact with an electron, the collision between two electrons can result in a sharp deviation in the direction of the electron as well as a sizeable loss of its kinetic energy.

Just as with heavy charged particles, electrons also are elastically scattered by collisions with nuclei. Due to the small mass of the electron, there is much greater probability than for heavy charged particles that it can, even at considerable distances from the nucleus, be scattered through large angles by the nuclear electric field. Because of the great difference in the masses, however, an electron loses only a small fraction of its energy in one of these elastic collisions with a nucleus. Numerous encounters of this sort result in "multiple scattering" and account for the tortuous paths of electrons revealed in cloud-chamber photographs and nuclear emulsions. As a result of such behavior the actual path length of an electron may be as much as four times the thickness of absorber traversed.

For electrons of several million electron volts or greater, loss of energy through the radiative process of bremsstrahlung emission becomes another important type of inelastic nuclear collision (the process of bremsstrahlung production was covered in some detail in Section II.2.C.). This is a much larger effect for electrons than that observed in the stopping of heavy charged particles. When an electron approaches the electric field of the nucleus it experiences both deflection and acceleration, resulting in the emission of radiation. The ratio of the energy loss of the incoming electrons by radiation to that lost by ionization in an absorber of atomic number Z is roughly equal to $EZ/800$, where E is the electron energy in millions of electron volts. Even at low energies of about 1 M.e.V. it can be seen that radiation losses are appreciable in stopping materials of high Z. For the range of energies encountered in most beta emitters, the production of bremsstrahlung radiation can be kept at a reasonably low level by using low-Z absorbing materials such as aluminum or beryllium.

Although of much less relative importance, still another type of energy-loss phenomenon occurs when fast electrons strike solids. There is emitted a visible radiation, called Čerenkov radiation after its discoverer (42). It has been described qualitatively as an electromagnetic shock wave analogous to that produced when a projectile travels through air at a speed greater than that of sound.

B. ABSORPTION OF BETA PARTICLES

Absorption Curve of Beta Spectrum. For beta rays of a given maximum energy, the absorption of the particles is very nearly characterized by an exponential relationship

$$\mathbf{R}_t = \mathbf{R}_0 e^{-\mu d} \qquad (23)$$

where $\mathbf{R}_d$ is the counting rate observed through the absorber and $\mathbf{R}_0$ the counting rate without any absorber. The absorber thickness in centimeters is given by d and the absorption coefficient in cm.$^{-1}$ by μ. This exponential law, which is a fortuitous consequence of the combined effects of scattering and of a continuous spectrum, is reasonably accurate except for the very beginning and the tail portion of the absorption curve. Since the scattering observed for beta rays depends on the geometrical arrangement of the sample, the detector, and the absorber, it is true that the exact shape of the absorption curve will, likewise, depend on these parameters.

A typical beta-ray absorption curve is shown in Figure 15. This shows a

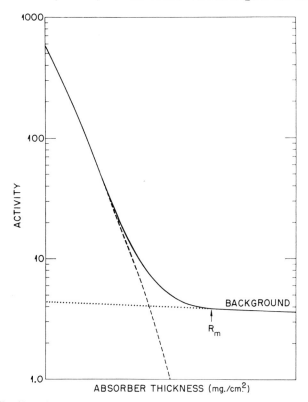

Fig. 15. Semilog plot of beta-ray activity observed through different thicknesses of absorber. The background is a typical one arising from the presence of gamma rays and bremsstrahlung. R_m is called the maximum range, representing the point at which the beta intensity goes to zero. The dashed curve shows the shape when background is subtracted.

single beta-ray group with a background resulting mainly from accompanying gamma rays. The gamma-ray background rarely exceeds 1 or 2% of the maximum beta counting rate since most argon-filled counters and air-filled ionization chambers are about 100 times more efficient for beta rays than for medium-energy gamma rays. This tail also contains some bremsstrahlung, but it is usually less than the gamma-ray background by about an order of magnitude. The point at which the curve meets the background contribution denoted by a dotted line in Figure 15 is the point of zero beta intensity and is called the maximum range R_m; one of the most reliable methods for determining R_m from an absorption curve is due to Feather (71).

Another useful concept is that of half-thickness, $d_{1/2}$. This is the thickness of absorber required to reduce the counting rate to one-half of its initial value, and from equation 25 it can be seen that $d_{1/2} = 0.693/\mu$. Very often the half-thickness is expressed in grams per square centimeter; hence, $d_{1/2} = 0.693\ \rho/\mu$, where ρ is the density of the absorber. Tables of half-thickness values in the literature usually refer to the initial portion of the absorption curves.

Although the use of absorption curves for measuring beta-ray energies is almost completely outdated, in the absence of electron spectrographs or of equipment for doing pulse-height analysis, absorption curves serve as a qualitative means of energy determination.

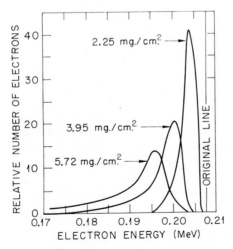

Fig. 16. Transmission through mica of the monoenergetic electrons from the 0.2065-MeV conversion line of RaB. The peak positions give the most probable energy losses. The most probable and average energy losses are different as a result of the asymmetric distributions [data from Evans (65), p. 622].

Range-Energy Relations. As a result of the multiple scattering and the large straggling effects, a precise theoretical treatment of the range–energy relations for electrons is precluded. The severity of the straggling encountered in electron absorption measurements is illustrated in Figure 16, where the transmission of monoenergetic conversion electrons is shown for different thicknesses of mica absorber. For the thicker absorbers the maximum peak shifts toward lower energies and spreads out considerably.

We observed in Part 1.A of this section that the range curve for a heavy charged particle likewise shows the presence of straggling, but it is a much smaller effect than that for beta particles. In the case of an alpha particle, the fractional energy lost as a result of an ionizing collision with an electron is of the order of the ratio of the masses, $\sim m_0/M$, where m_0 is the electron rest mass and M the mass of the alpha particle. Consequently, the alpha particle continues on in a very nearly straight path as it experiences these encounters, and the straggling effects are not too great. For an electron, effectively as much as one-half* its kinetic energy may be lost in an ionizing collision; and, in addition, any fraction of its energy could be lost as a result of a radiative collision. This latter mode occurs much less often than does ionization, but since the amount of energy lost in radiative collisions can take on such varied values, it too becomes an important cause of straggling.

Katz and Penfold (121) have recently made a thorough investigation of the range–energy relations. After compiling all the known data they arrived at the following empirical relationships:

$$R_m(\text{mg./cm.}^2) = 412\ E^{1.265-0.0954\ \ln E} \qquad E < 2.5\ \text{MeV} \qquad (24)$$

$$R_m(\text{mg./cm.}^2) = 530\ E - 106 \qquad E > 2.5\ \text{MeV} \qquad (25)$$

Here E is either the energy in millions of electron volts of a monoenergetic electron or the end-point beta-ray energy. Although there is some evidence that positron (β^+) ranges are slightly higher for a given energy particle, these relations are usually satisfactory for them. In Figure 17 we show the range–energy relation for beta particles and electrons in aluminum, based on these expressions.

Another important aspect to be considered in dealing with the behavior of electrons is *backscattering*. A significant fraction of the electrons that strike any material may be reflected back at large angles. Hence, it is advantageous to use a thin source backing of a low-Z material in order to reduce the number of electrons that are backscattered into the detector.

---

* This fraction is based on the fact that, following collision, the faster of the two electrons is arbitrarily identified as the "incoming" electron.

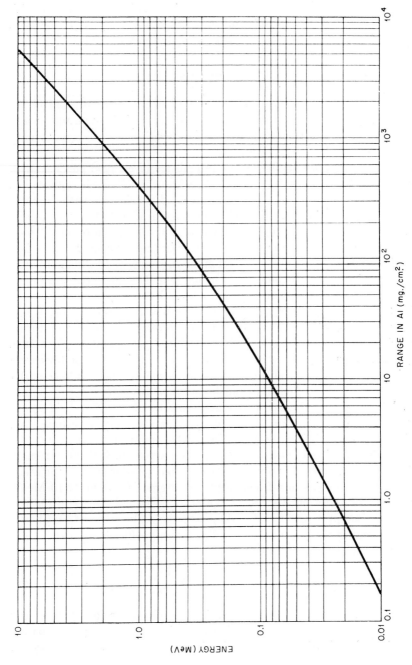

Fig. 17. Range–energy relation for electrons and beta particles in aluminum.

Much more extensive treatments of the interactions of electrons with matter are given by Evans (65) and by Mott and Massey (159). Detailed reviews have been given by Bothe (24) and by Bethe and Ashkin (13).

3. Gamma Rays

It is generally agreed that the interactions of photons with matter are independent of their origin and depend only upon their quantum energy (65). In this section, therefore, the term *gamma ray* will be synonymous with any type of electromagnetic radiation.

In the preceding discussion on the interaction of charged particles with matter, we saw that even in relatively thin absorbers their energy was lost through a large number of encounters, most of which were with the electrons of the absorbing material. This many-step process does not usually occur for gamma rays passing through similar absorbers. In principle, photons are either absorbed or scattered away from their original direction in a single interaction. The result is that gamma rays in a well-collimated beam are absorbed in a truly exponential fashion and show no maximum range, that is, equation 25 is adhered to rigorously.

Another marked difference in the ways in which charged particles and gamma rays interact with matter is in the amount of primary ionization they produce. The primary ionization produced by a photon occurs in a single step when it removes an electron from an atom by a photoelectric collision or a Compton collision. The swift secondary electron ejected by this process may have almost as much energy as the primary photon; and indeed, for all practical purposes, we may consider all the effects of photons as resulting from ionization produced by these secondary electrons (e.g., a 1-MeV electron produces $\sim$ 30,000 ion pairs in coming to rest).

Fano (70) has listed twelve possible processes by which the electromagnetic field of a gamma ray may interact with matter. However, in the range of gamma-ray energies most frequently encountered (up to about 10 MeV), only three of these effects are of major importance—the photoelectric effect, the Compton effect, and pair production. Then, for practical purposes we may write the total mass absorption coefficient, μ_{tot} (cm.^{2}/g.), for removal of gamma rays from a beam as

$$\mu_{tot} = \mu_{pe} + \mu_c + \mu_{pp} \qquad (26)$$

where μ_{pe}, μ_c, and μ_{pp} refer to the partial coefficients for the photoelectric effect, the Compton effect, and pair production, respectively. A separate discussion of each of these effects is given below. For a more thorough coverage see, for example, references 55, 65, and 105.

A. PHOTOELECTRIC EFFECT

The *photoelectric interaction* is the most important process for stopping gamma rays below about 100 keV. In this interaction an incident photon is totally absorbed by a bound electron resulting in the ejection of the electron from the atom with a kinetic energy E_e of

$$E_e = h\nu - E_B \qquad (27)$$

where $h\nu$ is the energy of the incoming photon and E_B is the binding energy of the ejected electron. This process is represented schematically in Figure 18.

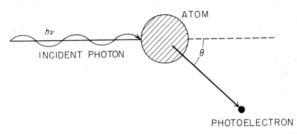

Fig. 18. Schematic representation of the photoelectric effect. The incident photon is completely absorbed, resulting in the bound electron being ejected from the atom at an angle θ with kinetic energy $E_e = h\nu - B_e$. Recoil of the entire residual atom provides momentum conservation.

For total absorption of the incident electromagnetic quantum, it is necessary that the electron struck be in a bound state. Only then can momentum be conserved by the recoil of the entire residual atom. It follows that the tightly bound electrons in the K shell account for a large part of the photoelectric cross section ($\sim 80\%$), provided the energy of the photon exceeds the K-shell binding energy. Following a photoelectric interaction one always observes the characteristic x rays and Auger electrons resulting from the filling of the vacancy in the inner shell.

Because of the difficulty encountered in a theoretical treatment of the photoelectric effect, much of the knowledge on this subject is of an empirical nature. Both the theory and experiment do show, however, that the partial absorption coefficient for the photoelectric process varies with the Z of the absorber (between Z^4 and Z^5, depending on the photon energy) and with about the cube of the photon energy. A crude but sometimes useful approximation is given by

$$\mu_{pe} \simeq aZ^4/(h\nu)^3 \qquad (28)$$

where a is a constant. A sharp discontinuity in the smooth trend of this absorption coefficient with energy occurs at the point at which the photon energy $h\nu$ becomes less than the binding energy of some of the electrons. This sudden change in the absorption coefficient is due to the decrease in the number of electrons which can be ejected. Use is made of these so-called "critical absorption edges" and their variation from element to element to identify the atomic number of an x-ray emitter. In Figure 41 of Section VI.1.C. is shown a plot of the partial absorption coefficients in NaI for the photoelectric, Compton, and pair production processes, along with the total mass absorption coefficient, as a function of the photon energy.

B. COMPTON SCATTERING

The *Compton effect* may be considered as an elastic collision of a photon against an electron. However, contrary to the requirements of the photoelectric process, the Compton interaction can occur with either free electrons or with those bound in an atom. In practice, if the electron is bound, the theory is simply limited to those cases for which the atomic binding energy of the struck electron is small compared with the energy of the incident photon. Most practical cases fall in this latter region, but in the limited number of cases that do not, the photoelectric cross section is

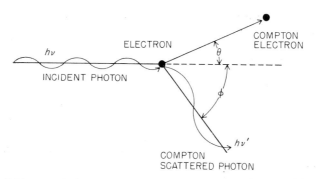

Fig. 19. Schematic representation of Compton scattering off a free electron. The incident photon is scattered at an angle ϕ with a decreased energy $h\nu'$. The electron is deflected at an angle θ with kinetic energy $h\nu - h\nu'$.

usually much larger than the Compton scattering cross section and, hence, the latter is of only minor importance. The photoelectric effect occurs predominantly with the K and L electrons of an atom, producing a relatively large number of characteristic x rays; but Compton scattering generally involves the outer electrons, resulting in few K and L x rays except in the cases of very light elements.

A diagram of the Compton scattering process is shown in Figure 19. A photon of initial energy $E = h\nu$ strikes an electron and is deflected at an angle ϕ with a decreased energy $E' = h\nu$. The electron goes off at an angle

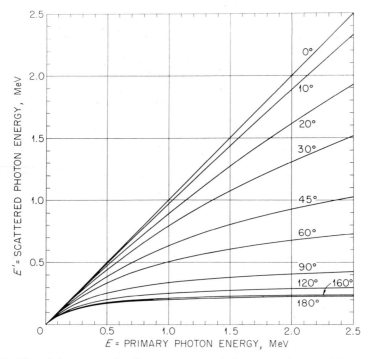

Fig. 20. Plot of the energy of a Compton-scattered photon as a function of the energy of the incident photon for several selected angles.

θ with kinetic energy $E_e = h\nu - h\nu'$. The paths of all three particles lie in the same plane as a result of momentum conservation requirements; and from these requirements the following very useful expression is obtained for the energy $(h\nu')$ of the degraded photon

$$h\nu' = \frac{h\nu}{1 + (h\nu/m_0c^2)(1 - \cos\phi)} \tag{29}$$

where $m_0c^2 = 0.51$ MeV. An evaluation of this equation for selected angles between 0 and 180° is shown in Figure 20 where the energy of the scattered photon is plotted as a function of the energy of the primary photon. Note that as the angle ϕ varies from 0 to 180°, the energy of the scattered photon varies from the initial value of $h\nu$ to its minimum value; also, note that the curves for the energies of scattered photons cluster for all the large-angle scattering. This latter effect gives rise to the familiar *backscatter peak* observed in gamma-ray spectra taken with an NaI spectrometer (cf., Section VI.1.C.).

Another interesting relationship that arises from the momentum conservation requirements is in the shift in wavelength of the primary and scattered photons. This Compton shift in wavelength is given by

$$\lambda' - \lambda = \frac{1}{h\nu'} - \frac{1}{h\nu} = \frac{1}{m_0 c^2}(1 - \cos \phi) \tag{30}$$

where λ' and λ are the wavelengths of the scattered and primary photons, respectively. In the case of the Compton shift in energy, which can be obtained by equation 29, the energy of the scattered photon is strongly dependent on the energy of the incoming photon. In sharp contrast, however, we observe that in a given direction the Compton shift in wavelength, $\lambda' - \lambda$, is totally independent of the energy of the incident photon.

The differential scattering cross section for a photon was first explained with reasonable accuracy by the classical picture of Thomson scattering (e.g., see reference 65). This picture is true only as long as the quantum energy $h\nu$ of the photon is large compared with the binding energy of the atomic electrons to be scattered, yet is small compared with their rest energy, $m_0 c^2 = 0.51$ MeV.

In 1929, Klein and Nishina (126) were able to apply Dirac's new relativistic theory of the electron to this problem and to develop a solution which is in excellent agreement with experiment over a broad energy range. An extensive number of curves and tables of values of the quantities derived from the Klein-Nishina equations has been compiled by Nelms (162).

C. PAIR PRODUCTION

A third way in which photons interact with matter is by *pair production* which has a photon energy threshold of 1.02 MeV. In this process the incident photon disappears and its energy $h\nu$ becomes the *total* energy of the newly formed electron–positron pair. Of the total energy, $2m_0 c^2$ (1.02 MeV) is accounted for by the rest masses of the electron and positron, and the kinetic energy $h\nu - 2m_0 c^2$ may be shared in any proportion between them. In general, the positron will get a slightly larger fraction of the energy since it is repelled by the nucleus while the electron is attracted. At high energies there is a strong tendency for the particles to be ejected in the forward direction.

Pair production can occur only in the field of charged particles, usually nuclei, although to some extent in the field of an electron. The close proximity of the charged particle is mandatory to permit momentum conservation. A schematic representation of the process is shown in Figure 21.

The pair-production process is conveniently pictured in terms of the positive and negative energy states of the electron presented by Dirac (see Section II.2.C.). The reader is referred to the work of Bethe and Heitler (14) for a quantum-mechanical solution of the phenomenon. Mathemati-

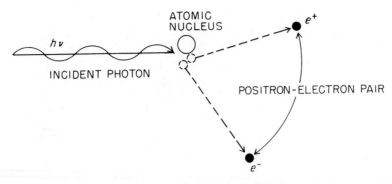

Fig. 21. Schematic representation of the pair-production process in a nuclear field. The incident photon is completely absorbed and a positron–electron pair emerge with a kinetic energy of $h\nu - 2m_0c^2$.

cally, the theory of pair production is almost identical with that of the bremsstrahlung process. In the latter, an electron undergoes a transition between two positive energy states, and a photon is emitted instead of being absorbed.

Pair production is always accompanied by the annihilation of the positron, in which process two gamma quanta of 0.51 MeV are usually emitted at 180° to each other (Section II.2.C.). Also associated with the process will be the appearance of the bremsstrahlung background as the electron and positron come to rest.

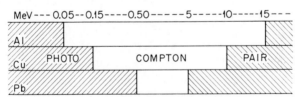

Fig. 22. Scheme showing energy regions in which the photoelectric effect, the Compton interaction, and pair production are predominant for three ranges of Z represented by aluminum, copper, and lead.

In Figure 22 we show a very generalized scheme of regions of Z and photon energy where the above-discussed modes of gamma-ray interactions with matter are predominant. The regions of low, medium, and high Z are represented by aluminum, copper, and lead, respectively.

4. Biological Effects of Radiation

Thus far we have thought of the stopping of radiations in matter and of the resulting effects only in terms of physical experimentation. However, the effects of radiation on biological systems is an aspect of great importance and one about which every experimenter working with radioactive materials should have some knowledge. The biological effects of radiation result from chemical changes in the cells caused by ionizations, excitations, dissociations, and atomic displacements. These are indeed drastic effects on a biological system, and in one sense, must in all cases be considered harmful. Even in very low doses, radiation seems to cause a shortening of the expected life span of animals to the extent of about 10^{-4} life spans per roentgen of total body exposure (241). It has also been observed that the genetic mutation rate increases with exposure to ionizing radiation and that there is apparently no threshold level of radiation below which genetic effects do not occur (154).

Such observations are not intended to discourage the experimenter from carrying on research in which some exposure is inevitable. It must be remembered that at all times we are being exposed to radiation, from both cosmic rays and radioactive elements in the earth's crust, at an intensity level which has apparently remained rather constant for millions of years. In many cases, the radiation dosage acquired in the laboratory will be only a small perturbation on that resulting from our natural environment. Often a stronger incentive for care in working with radioactivity is not concern over personal exposure to radiation, but rather in prevention of cross contamination that could obviate the value of the data obtained in an experiment.

In light of what has been said, it would seem logical to expect the experimenter to possess a knowledge of radiation hazards and of the effects they can produce. Our only efforts here will be to define the basic units of radiation dosage and to give the recommended maximum personal exposure for each type. There are many excellent papers, e.g., references 115, 154, and 192, which deal with this subject and to which we refer the reader for a more extensive treatment than that given below. There are in addition Federal rules and regulations (72) for protection of employees and the public against radiation. Overman and Clark (166) have given considerable attention to safety practices to be followed when working with radioactivity.

The common units of radiation dosage and their definitions are as follows:

1. Roentgen (abbreviated r.) = that quantity of x or gamma radiation such that the associated corpuscular emission per 0.001293 g. of air produces, in air, ions carrying 1 e.s.u. of quantity of electricity of either sign. This is often expressed in terms of milliroentgens (mr.), i.e., 10^{-3} r.

1 r. $= 2.093 \times 10^9$ ion pairs/cm.^{3} (air, STP)

$= 1.61 \times 10^{12}$ ion pairs/g. (air)

$= 6.77 \times 10^4$ MeV/cm.^{3} (air, STP)

$= 5.24 \times 10^7$ MeV/g. (air)

$= 83.8$ ergs/g. (air)

$= 2.0 \times 10^{-16}$ cal./g. (air)

2. Rad (radiation absorbed dose) = unit of absorbed dose of any type radiation producing energy absorption equivalent to 100 ergs/g. of tissue.
3. Rem (roentgen equivalent man) = that quantity of any type radiation which when absorbed by man produces an effect *equivalent* to that of one roentgen of x or gamma radiation. This is often expressed in terms of millirem (mrem), i.e., 10^{-3} rem.
4. RBE (relative biological effectiveness) = the ratio of x ray or gamma dose to the dose that is required to produce the same biological effect by the radiation in question.

In column 1 of Table II we list various types of radiation and in column 2 show the RBE for each type. Column 3 shows the corresponding units of dosage for 1 rad of each type of these radiations (dose in rems = dose in rads $\times$ RBE factor). Note the very high RBE for alpha particles. This accounts for the fact that extreme caution must be exercised by those

TABLE II

RADIATION DOSAGE EQUIVALENTS

(Dose in rems = dose in rads $\times$ RBE factor)

Type of radiation	RBE	Equivalents
Gamma or x	1	1 r. = 1 rad = 1 rem
Beta	1	1 rad = 1 rem
Thermal neutrons	5	1 rad = 5 rem
Fast neutrons	10	1 rad = 10 rem
Alpha particles	20	1 rad = 20 rem

working with alpha-emitting radioactivities. The large RBE for fast neutrons results from secondary effects, as might be expected. When fast neutrons strike hydrogenous material, the resulting recoil protons produce a large amount of ionization.

Table III gives the maximum permissible flux for occupational exposure to various types of ionizing radiations. The data were tabulated in this manner by Morgan (154) and are based on dose values recommended in

TABLE III
MAXIMUM PERMISSIBLE FLUX FOR OCCUPATIONAL EXPOSURE TO VARIOUS TYPES
OF IONIZING RADIATIONS[a]

Type radiation	RBE	Average exposure rate[b] (mrad/wk.)	Approximate flux to give a maximum permissible exposure in an 8-hour day[c]
X and gamma rays	1	100	$(1400/E)$ photons/cm.²/sec. in free air at 0° C. (error $<13\%$ for $E = 0.07–2$ MeV)
Beta rays and electrons	1	100	$(4.3 \times 10^7)/(\text{RBE})P^d$ electrons or beta rays/cm.²/sec. incident on tissue ($\simeq$23 electrons or 15 β per cm.²/sec. of 1 MeV energy)
Thermal neutrons	2.5	40	700 thermal neutrons/cm.²/sec. incident on tissue
Fast neutrons	10	10	19 neutrons of 2 MeV energy/cm.²/sec. incident on tissue
Alpha particles	10	10	$4.3 \times 10^7/(\text{RBE})P$ alpha particles/cm.²/sec. incident on tissue ($\simeq$0.005 alpha particles of 5 MeV/cm.²/sec.)
Protons	10	10	$4.3 \times 10^7/(\text{RBE})P$ protons/cm.²/sec. incident on tissue ($\simeq$0.06 protons of 5 MeV/cm.²/sec.)
Heavy ions	20	5	$4.3 \times 10^7/(\text{RBE})P$ heavy ions/cm.²/sec. ($\simeq$0.0002 oxygen ions of 5 MeV/cm.²/sec.)

[a] Values of flux corresponding to dose values as recommended in 1959 by the National Committee on Radiation Protection and by the International Commission on Radiological Protection.

[b] Average occupational exposure rate permissible to blood-forming organs (essentially total body exposure), gonads, and eyes of persons of age 18 or over. These values may be averaged over a year, provided the RBE dose in any 13 weeks does not exceed 3 rem (rem = RBE $\times$ rad). All values in columns 3 and 4 may be increased by a factor of 6 if the exposure is primarily to the skin, thyroid, or bone. They may be increased by a factor of 3 if the exposure is limited to organs other then blood-forming organs, gonads, or eyes.

[c] Maximum permissible exposure rate based on a 20 mrem RBE dose delivered to tissue in an 8-hour day (= 2.5/RBE mrad/hr.) and assuming $W = 35$ for alpha and 34 for beta and secondary electrons (see footnote d). The rad in soft tissue is considered to correspond to an energy absorption of 100 ergs/g.

[d] P is the stopping power in units of electron volts per gram per cm.² of tissue. It can be calculated from the following equation.

$$P = S_a W P_t/\rho_a \simeq 2.7 \times 10^4 S_a P_t \text{ eV/g./cm.}^2$$

where S_a is the specific ionization of the ionizing particle in air, W is the energy required to produce a pair of ions, P_t is the mass stopping power of tissue relative to air, and ρ_a is the density of air for which S_a is given.

1959 by the National Committee on Radiation Protection and by the International Commission on Radiological Protection (192).

IV. PRODUCTION OF RADIONUCLIDES

Because of the extremely long life ($>$ 10^9 years) of the universe, most of the tracers which were produced "in the beginning" have since decayed. With the exception of the few survivors which almost all lie at the upper end of the periodic table and minute amounts of other species generated by cosmic ray bombardment, all of the isotopes used today must be "made to order." These syntheses can be performed by means of nuclear reactions in which particles (neutrons, protons, alpha particles, etc.) are caused to interact with a *target*, a substance chosen to yield the desired nuclide.

Before exploring the machinery and crafts of this new "alchemy," we will discuss the basic considerations of nuclear reactions. Our treatment will begin with the energetic or thermodynamic aspects of interacting nuclei and include the concept of cross section or probability of a nuclear reaction. We will touch on some of the most important theories and mechanisms of nuclear reactions. Next, specific reactions will be considered. Finally, nuclear reactors and charged-particle accelerators will be described, together with the techniques for their use.

1. Nuclear Reactions

There is a striking parallel between nuclear and chemical reactions. The physicist observes the results of interaction of the bombarding particle with the target. Analogously, the chemist studies the transformation of the initial reactants into final products. In both classes of phenomena, energy conservation is observed. However, the scale of energies is fantastically disparate: nuclear reactions involve energy changes of millions of electron volts, chemical reactions only a few electron volts. Further, it is possible and fruitful to detect and study the individual particles involved in nuclear events, whereas chemical investigations almost always deal with vast assemblages of atoms and molecules.

Again emphasizing the chemical–nuclear correspondence, we may symbolize a nuclear reaction with a "balanced" equation essentially identical to a chemical equation:

$$Co^{59} + H^2 \rightarrow Co^{60} + H^1$$

To balance this type of equation the sum of the mass or nucleon number, A, must be the same on both sides of the equal sign. A corollary to this law of the conservation of A is conservation of proton number, as long as one considers nuclear reactions at low or moderately high energies. It is only with high-energy (200 MeV or higher) nuclear reactions or with beta decay that neutrons or protons are transformed into each other. Even in these cases total charge is conserved. The above equation can be given in a convenient shorthand treatment:

$$Co^{59}(d,p)Co^{60}$$

In this convention the target is always given first, the parentheses contain the bombarding particle and the emergent light particle, and last comes the product nucleus. The most common light particles are abbreviated as follows:

H^1, p proton H^3, t triton
H^2, d deuteron He^4, α alpha particle

A. ENERGETICS OF NUCLEAR REACTIONS

Just as the ΔH of a chemical reaction arises from the making or breaking of chemical bonds or rearrangements in orbital electronic configuration, so the energy, Q, of a nuclear reaction results from nucleonic rearrangements. The Q will manifest itself as kinetic energy of the products if the reaction releases energy—is *exoergic*. Such an energy release must be compensated for by an equivalent mass decrease:

$$Q = \text{(atomic mass of reactants)} - \text{(atomic mass of products)}$$

(The calculation of the mass–energy conversion utilizes the famous $E = mc^2$.) If, on the other hand, the products are heavier than reactants, the reaction will be *endoergic* and the bombarding particle must be given additional kinetic energy to make the reaction go. Thus Q is positive for an exoergic process, negative for an endoergic one.

Before performing a new chemical reaction, a chemist may consult a tabulation of standard heats of reaction in order to confirm the thermodynamic feasibility of his experiment. Similarly, a nuclear chemist will look at tabulated mass data before attempting a nuclear reaction. Of the great variety of mass tables, Wapstra's (229) is the most complete and up to date; the Nuclear Data Sheets (230) should be scanned for the recent data. These mass values come both from mass spectrometric measurements, and from precision determinations of Q values of nuclear reactions or beta-decay energies. For predicting the Q values of reactions which lead to new nuclides, tables of masses have been computed using semi-empirical mass equations (cf., Section II.2.A.). In Cameron's set of tables (36) the predictions are expressed in terms of the mass excess, the neutron, proton, or alpha binding energies, and the beta-decay energy. Let us illustrate the use of these tables by predicting the Q value for the reaction

$$Si^{30} + n \rightarrow Al^{30} + p + Q$$

The mass of Si^{30}, the neutron, and the proton are well known, but that of Al^{30}, an unknown nuclide, is not. From Cameron's table we find that the beta-decay energy of Al^{30} should be 9.23 MeV. This is equivalent to the mass difference $(Al^{30} - Si^{30})$ of

$$\frac{9.23 \text{ MeV}}{931 \text{ MeV/mass unit}} = 0.0099 \text{ mass units}$$

Adding this to the mass of Si^{30} we find

Si^{30} mass	29.98325
$Al^{30} - Si^{30}$ mass diff.	0.0099
Al^{30} mass	29.99315

Then the Q of the above reaction is

$Q = [(\text{mass of } Si^{30} + \text{mass of neutron}) - (\text{mass of } Al^{30} + \text{mass of proton})]$
$$\times 931 \text{ MeV/mass unit}$$
$= [(29.98235 + 1.00899) - (29.99315 + 1.00814)] \times 931$
$= -8.44 \text{ MeV}$

Thus the reaction is endoergic by 8.44 MeV.

Even if the bombarding particle possesses sufficient kinetic energy to satisfy the energetics of the reaction, it still may not proceed. There are two further considerations.

Conservation of linear momentum requires that the composite system of bombarding particle plus target nucleus must receive some kinetic energy of recoil just as would a struck billiard ball. Because of this, the entire kinetic energy of the incident particle cannot go into exciting the composite system and promoting the reaction. To obtain the corrected energy of excitation E_{ex}, let us write on the basis of conservation of linear momentum

$$m_p \, v_p = m_c \, v_c \tag{31}$$

where m_p and v_p are the mass and velocity of the incident particle and m_c and v_c the same quantities for the composite system after collision. Then, from conservation of energy

$$^1/_2 \, m_p \, v_p{}^2 = {}^1/_2 \, m_c \, v_c{}^2 + E_{ex} \tag{32}$$

Multiplying by mc/mc and transposing, we obtain

$$(^1/_2 m_c \, m_p \, v_p{}^2 - {}^1/_2 \, m_c{}^2 \, v_c{}^2)/m_c = E_{ex} \tag{32}$$

Substituting for $m_c \, v_c$ from equation 1 gives

$$^1/_2 \, m_p \, v_p{}^2 - {}^1/_2 \, (m_p{}^2 \, v_p{}^2)/m_c = E_{ex}$$
$$E_p - (m_p/m_c)E_p = E_{ex}$$

Since $m_c = m_p + m_t$ (where m_t is the mass of the target nucleus) the expression may be written

$$E_p [m_t/(m_t + m_p)] = E_{ex} \qquad (33)$$

Thus, the recoil loss is only significant for light-element targets or for so-called heavy-ion projectiles (such as N^{14}).

A positively-charged particle approaching the nucleus experiences a force due to Coulombic repulsion. This constitutes the Coulomb barrier referred to earlier in the discussion of alpha decay in Section II.2.B. If the bombarding particle penetrates the barrier it will come within the range of the attractive nuclear force; to use the jargon expression: it will fall into a "potential well." The height of the Coulomb barrier is:

$$V = Z_p Z_t e^2/(R_p + R_t) \qquad (34)$$

where the Z's are the charges and the R's are the radii of the particle and target nuclei.

The radius of the nucleus increases as nucleons are added to it. In fact, since the volume is approximately proportional to the nucleon number and since nuclei are in general spherical, the radius is given by

$$R = b A^{1/3} \qquad (35)$$

The value of b ranges from about 1.2×10^{-13} cm. to 1.6×10^{-13} cm., depending on A and on the method of measurement. However, rough calculations adequate for planning a nuclear reaction can be made, using an intermediate value of 1.4×10^{-13} cm. For protons bombarding an aluminum target this type of calculation yields a barrier height of ~ 4 MeV; for gold the barrier is ~ 14 MeV. Deuteron and triton barriers are almost the same as those for protons; alpha particle barriers are roughly twice as great, except for low-Z targets, such as O^{16}.

It is only correct from the classical point of view to state that no reaction will occur unless the Coulomb barrier is surmounted. Actually, according to the quantum-mechanical view, any charged particle striking the nucleus has a finite probability of penetrating or tunneling through the barrier. Of course, the lower the energy of the projectile relative to the barrier height, the smaller the probability of penetration (cf., Fig. 7). Note that a particle in penetrating into the nucleus (whether over or through the barrier) does not "use up" any of its energy in the process. Only the correction for recoil of the particle-target composite needs to be made to obtain the energy available for excitation. The absence of a Coulomb barrier for neutral particles allows neutron-induced reactions to proceed at very low incident energies.

B. CROSS SECTION

So far we have been concerned primarily with the energetic prerequisites for a nuclear reaction. All of these may be satisfied and yet the reaction may not be observed. Of course, this would imply a low reaction probability which corresponds in the chemical sense to a small reaction rate. For a quantitative treatment of nuclear reactions, the chemical k, or specific rate constant, is replaced by the cross-section σ, a parameter more consistent with the nuclear physicist's concern for individual particles. It is defined by the expression

$$N = I \, n \, \sigma \tag{36}$$

where N is the number of product nuclei formed per second; I is the intensity or flux of bombarding particles of a single energy per sec.-cm.^{2}; n is the number of target nuclei presented to the beam of incident particles; σ is the cross section for the specified event in units of cm.^{2}.

Cross sections vary with the energy of the incident particle. Figure 25 in Part 2.A. of this section shows the result of measuring σ as a function of incident particle energy for several reactions which occur when protons bombard Cu^{63}. Each curve is called the *excitation function* of that particular reaction and the *threshold* of the reaction is the energy at which the reaction first begins. Cross sections rarely are larger than a value corresponding roughly to the geometrical cross-sectional area of the nucleus or about 10^{-24} cm.^{2}. For convenience a cross section of 10^{-24} cm.^{2} is referred to as one *barn* or 1 b.; likewise 10^{-27} cm.^{2} is 1 *millibarn*, mb., and 10^{-30} cm.^{2} is 1 *microbarn*, μb. Equation 36 can be used for calculations of reaction yields unless the incident beam is attenuated or degraded in energy by passage through the target; in other words it is a "thin target" expression. Compilations of cross sections suitable for such calculations have been made for many different nuclear reactions over a wide range of incident energies (112, 113).

If a target is strongly absorbing but does not degrade the energy of the bombarding particle, an exponential form of equation 36 must be used:

$$N = I(1 - e^{-n\sigma}) \tag{37}$$

C. MECHANISMS OF NUCLEAR REACTIONS

We have alluded to the variation in σ for different target elements and for different bombarding particles. To explain these changes in cross section, a number of models of nuclear reactions have been constructed. In recent years a consolidation of these ideas has occurred, and the prospect for a truly unified theory of nuclear reactions seems good.

All nuclear reactions, regardless of the particular details of their mechanisms, have as their first steps the initial interaction or collision of the particle with the target nucleus. The incoming particle may either cause some change in the nucleus or it may be diffracted or refracted by the nucleus and emerge without inducing any nuclear excitation. This latter process is referred to as elastic scattering. A quantum-mechanical formalism referred to as the *R-matrix* or *partial-wave* theory has been developed to describe this beginning stage of a reaction. Although this treatment is mathematically correct it is not directly useful for the prediction of reaction cross sections, since its evaluation for a real case would involve the solution of a many-body problem, an impossible computational task. There has been some success recently in dealing with this problem by considering the incoming particle as moving in a complex potential which consists of two parts, $V(r)$, the real or refracting part which describes the interactions yielding elastic scattering, and $W(r)$, the imaginary or absorbing part which describes those events leading to nuclear reactions.

Once the incident particle has struck and penetrated into the nucleus it will begin to collide with nucleons. Then one of two possible chains of events may ensue:

1. In Figure 23a the incident particle strikes a nucleon (for example, a neutron), gives up most of its energy, and comes to rest in the nucleus. The struck nucleon moves across the nuclear volume and leaves the nucleus. This process is referred to as a type of *direct interaction;* the illustrated example is known by the specific title of *knock-on* process. The time scale for such an event is of the order of the transit time of a nucleon across the nucleus, approximately 10^{-21} sec.

2. In Figure 23b the incident particle strikes a nucleon, but only a glancing blow, and gives up a part of its energy. Both particles now move through the nucleus, undergoing many collisions. Eventually the initial kinetic energy is distributed uniformly or statistically throughout the nucleus. This excited system is called the *compound nucleus.* It ultimately de-excites by emitting one or more nucleons; by a gamma-ray decay to its ground state or by splitting into two roughly equal pieces—*nuclear fission.* Since the time for the decay of the compound nucleus is of the order of 10^{-12}–10^{-14} sec., all "memory" of the mode of formation of the composite system is lost.

As the above descriptions suggest, some of the products of a nuclear reaction may be produced by a direct interaction process and some following compound nucleus formation. Both effects may occur within one reaction event; specifically, the initial event may be a direct interaction, leaving the nucleus in an excited metastable state which is essentially a compound nucleus. The competition between the two processes depends strongly on the nature and kinetic energy of the bombarding particle as well as the

Z and A of the target. Particular cases will be cited in Part 2.A. of this section, in which one or the other mechanism predominates.

The preceding discussion of nuclear reactions is of necessity brief. For more elaborate treatments of concepts such as barrier penetration, cross section, and compound nucleus formation, texts such as that of Morrison (156) and Blatt and Weisskopf (20) should be consulted. A report on the

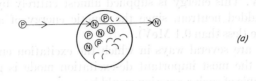

(a)

DIRECT INTERACTION

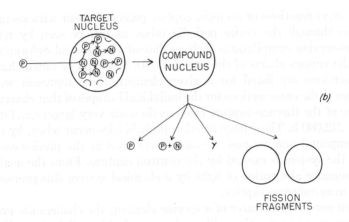

(b)

COMPOUND NUCLEUS

Fig. 23. Schematic illustrations of the two basic types of reaction mechanisms. P and N denote proton and neutron. (*a*) *A* *direct interaction* type, specifically a *knock-on* event. (*b*) the *compound* nucleus process.

current state of nuclear reaction theory, including extensive discussions of direct interaction processes, is contained in the proceedings of the Kingston Conference on Nuclear Structure (29). The summary paper by Weisskopf gives an excellent comprehensive view of the major accomplishments and problems of the field. An earlier conference on nuclear reactions was held in Amsterdam in 1955 (187).

2. Methods of Production

A. TYPES OF REACTIONS

Neutron Reactions. Neutrons interact very readily with nuclei because of the absence of a Coulomb barrier. If the neutrons are *thermal*, i.e., moving at velocities comparable to thermal atomic motion, they will fuse with the target nuclide to form a compound nucleus with an excitation energy of 6–8 MeV. This energy is supplied almost entirely by the binding energy of the added neutron, since the kinetic energy of a thermal neutron is negligible (less than 0.1 MeV).

There are several ways in which the excitation energy may be carried off, but the most important de-excitation mode is gamma-ray emission. An example of such a reaction would be

$$Co^{59} + n \rightarrow Co^{60} + \gamma \qquad [\text{or } \overset{*}{Co}^{59}(n,\gamma)Co^{60}]$$

These (n,γ) reactions or *radiative capture* processes occur with useful cross sections through the entire periodic table, as can be seen by reference to cross-section compilations such as that of Hughes and Schwartz (112) or to the various charts of the nuclides (84). It should be noted that when cross sections are listed for a given element, these represent weighted averages of the cross sections for the individual isotopes of that element.

Some of the thermal capture cross sections are very large; e.g., for Gd^{157}, $\sigma_{n,\gamma} = 242,000$ b. These huge reaction probabilities occur when, by chance, the compound nucleus possesses a discrete level at the precise energy to which the system is excited by the neutron capture. From the analogy to the resonance absorption of light by a chemical system this process is referred to as *resonance capture*.

When one needs a tracer of a specific element, the chances are probably 2:1 that an (n,γ) reaction will produce a suitable radioisotope. For such an application one would simply expose a sample of the natural element to a neutron flux. If, on the other hand, a specific nuclide is desired, it may be necessary to utilize a target enriched in the desired target isotope. As an example, thermal neutron irradiation of natural cadmium would result in a mixture of six radioactive cadmium isotopes

Cd^{106} (n,γ) Cd^{107}	$t_{1/2} = 6.7$ hr.
$Cd^{1\,8}$ $n,\gamma)$ Cd^{109}	$t_{1/2} = 1.3$ yr.
Cd^{110} (n,γ) Cd^{111m}	$t_{1/2} = 49$ min.
Cd^{112} (n,γ) Cd^{113m}	$t_{1/2} = 5$ yr.
Cd^{114} (n,γ) Cd^{115m} and Cd^{115}	$t_{1/2} = 43$ day and 54 hr.
Cd^{116} (n,γ) Cd^{117m} and Cd^{117}	$t_{1/2} = 3.0$ hr. and 50 min.

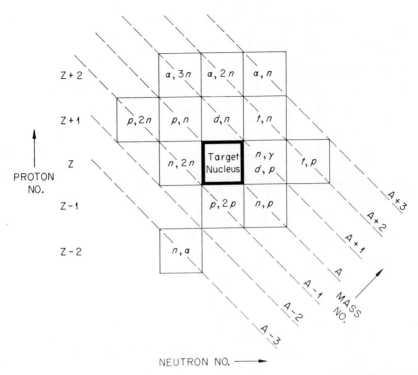

NEUTRON NO. ⟶

Fig. 24. Some important nuclear reactions induced by neutrons and charged particles
The representation is patterned after that of the G. E. Chart of the Nuclides (84).

Even after a week's decay, three species would still be present: Cd^{109}, Cd^{113m}, and Cd^{115m}. Such a mixture could be separated by making use of an electromagnetic separator (130). However, it is nearly always simpler to start with an enriched target.

Let us reconsider the question of de-exciting the compound nucleus formed by thermal neutron capture. In principle, heavy particles can carry off the energy as well as gamma rays. However, charged particle (p, d, α) emission is highly unlikely since the barrier to a particle leaving the nucleus is the same as that confronting an approaching charged particle, and with only 7 MeV of excitation the barrier penetration probability is low. On the other hand, neutron emission can occur readily due to the absence of a Coulomb barrier. Such a process leaves the nucleus untransmuted, and thus is an elastic scattering process. The neutron may not remove the entire excitation energy but instead carry the excited nucleus to a lower energy excited state which would in turn de-excite by gamma-ray emission to the ground state. This is called inelastic neutron scattering. Charged particle emission can

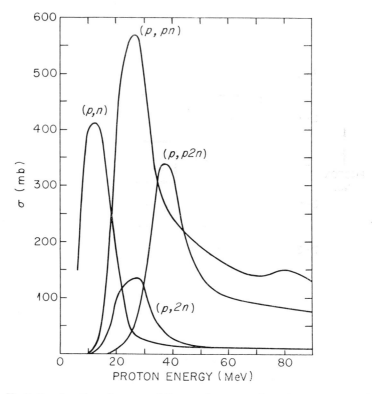

Fig. 25. Excitation functions for some of the reactions occurring when protons bombard Cu^{63} [from J. M. Meadows, *Phys. Rev.*, **91**, 885 (1953); used in this form by Friedlander and Kennedy (78)].

occur following thermal neutron capture in a few very light elements, e.g., $B^{10}(n,\alpha)Li^7$, $Li^6(n,\alpha)H^3$.

As the kinetic energy of the neutron increases, the cross section for the (n,γ) reaction decreases. However, as the energy reaches 2 or 3 MeV, reactions such as (n,p), (n,α), and $(n,2n)$ become feasible with targets of moderate A. With 14 MeV neutrons, even heavy-element targets will undergo these reactions. Some specific examples are $Fe^{56}(n,p)Mn^{56}$, $Ge^{74}(n,\alpha)Zn^{71}$, and $Mo^{100}(n,2n)Mo^{99}$. Figure 24 illustrates the general versatility of these reactions. Recent investigations of the mechanisms of these reactions indicate that both direct interaction and compound nucleus formation occur.

In recent years there have been extensive measurements of cross sections for these reactions induced by 14.5-MeV neutrons; this is the energy of the neutrons obtained (in the forward direction) from the $H^3(d,n)$ reaction. A large number of these measured values are given in the reports of Coleman *et al.* (47), Paul and Clarke (173), Wille and Fink (237), and Bayhurst and Prestwood (5). The latter pair have determined (n,p), (n,α), and $(n,2n)$ cross sections for neutron energies ranging from 7 to 20 MeV. To help systematize this plethora of data, Gardner has compiled all available (n,p) and (n,α) cross sections (81, 82).

Note that for neutron reactions equation 36 can be used for estimating yields, since the neutron energy and hence the cross sections will not be affected by passage through the sample. For targets with cross sections of 1000 b. or higher, significant attenuation of the flux by absorption does occur.

Charged Particle Reactions. A great variety of charged particle reactions can be performed which lead to a broad spectrum of products. In general, at low bombarding energies (5–10 MeV) only a single nucleon is emitted after collision. At higher energies two or more particles emerge. When the incident particle reaches several hundred million electron volts in energy, many particles are emitted, either singly or as fragments.

The competition between the various reactions induced by a single bombarding particle is illustrated by Figure 25, which shows the excitation functions for the reactions produced when protons bombard Cu^{63}. Note that the (p,n) reaction has the lowest threshold due to the barrier for charged particle emission, and that up to 10 MeV only the single product, Zn^{63}, will be produced. As the bombarding energy is increased, a mixture of radioactivities will be produced. By referring to the excitation function, one can choose a bombarding energy that will enhance the relative yield of the desired species. The (p,n) and (p,pn) products, Zn^{63} and Cu^{62}, could be separated chemically; however, since the isotopes that result from (p,n) and $(p,2n)$ processes are of the same element, one must depend on difference in half-life to obtain a source of a single isotope. Here again, electromagnetic isotope separators may prove useful.

With composite projectiles, such as the d, t, He^3, or α, a new type of reaction is encountered, which is called *stripping*. This process, a special type of direct interaction, occurs when the target nucleus strips off one or more nucleons from the incoming projectile. What remains of the bombarding particle continues on its trajectory with only a small loss in kinetic energy. This process is very important for low-energy deuterons. The deuteron is dumbbell-like in shape with a relatively large neutron-proton distance. As it approaches the nucleus, the deuteron is strongly polarized by the nuclear Coulomb field with the proton end repelled; the neutron thus enters the nucleus and is "stripped" off. Such a (d,p) reaction can occur at energies several million electron volts below the barrier energy, but if the bombarding energy is well above the barrier, the proton can be stripped with equal ease. The (t,p) or (H^3, H^1) reaction seems to behave as a double neutron stripping process. Alpha-particle stripping reactions occur with much smaller cross sections since the He^4 nucleus is quite tightly bound. The inverse of deuteron stripping, a process known as *pickup*, can occur with proton bombardment. The proton may graze the target nucleus, remove a neutron, and then emerge as a deuteron.

It has become possible in recent years to accelerate ions heavier than He nuclei, such as Li^6, Li^7, C^{12}, O^{16}, N^{14}, Ar^{40}. By bombarding with these "heavy ions," one can synthesize nuclides on the neutron-deficient side of stability that could not be reached with the simpler particles. These particles permit "leapfrogging" over regions in which no stable target elements exist. This is graphically illustrated by the work of Ghiorso *et al.* (85) in their nuclear synthesis of element 103, lawrencium, in which the long-lived transuranium element, californium, was utilized as the target. The successful reaction was probably

$$Cf^{252}(B^{11}, 6n)Lw^{257}$$

Heavy-ion reactions of this type proceed predominantly by compound nucleus formation since it is quite improbable for a massive projectile to transfer most of its momentum to a single nucleon. However, reactions analogous to stripping and pickup do occur with heavy ions, although they are more commonly referred to as *nucleon transfer*. Radiative capture of charged particles, for example, (p,γ) and (d,γ), and also photonuclear reactions like (γ,n) and (γ,p) can take place, but with relatively small cross sections.

To maximize the yield of a charged particle reaction product, thick targets should be used to utilize more fully the beam of incident particles. However, this complicates prediction of the reaction yield, since the incident particle energy, and hence the cross section, will be varying continuously. Some thick target yields have been carefully determined for specific reactions and energies: Martin *et al.* (147), report several measured values and a large number of estimated values of thick target yields for (p,n) and $(p,2n)$ reactions; Gruverman and Kruger (93) give measured yields for 17 deuteron-produced nuclides.

Fission. Nuclear fission is a spectacular producer of radioisotopes. The thermal neutron fission of U^{235}, for example, yields nuclides ranging from $Z = 30$ to $Z = 65$, with masses from 72 to 161. This prolific nature of the process results from the variety of fission modes as well as from the production of daughter radioisotopes by the decay of the initial fragments.

The fission products invariably decay by β^- emission since they are rich in neutrons. Their daughters will in turn β^- decay until a stable nucleus is reached. These decay sequences are called *fission product decay chains* and a typical example is the mass 88 chain:

$$Br^{88} \xrightarrow{16 \text{ sec.}} Kr^{88} \xrightarrow{2.8 \text{ hr.}} Rb^{88} \xrightarrow{18 \text{ min.}} Sr^{88} \text{ (stable)}$$

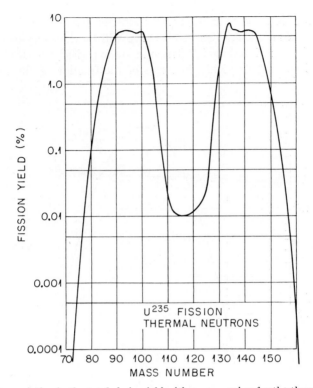

Fig. 26. The variation in the total chain yield with mass number for the thermal neutron fission of U^{235} [Katcoff (120)].

Such decay chains have been studied extensively since the discovery of fission, not only as to their decay properties, but also as to the yield of each member of the chain and the total yield per fission event.

The variation of total chain yield with mass number for thermal fission of U^{235} shows an interesting double-peaked pattern (Fig. 26). [These curves are from the excellent compilation of Katcoff (120).] This behavior, characteristic of fission at low excitation energy, means that the most probable splitting mode is into fragments of mass about 95 and 135, that is, *asymmetric fission*. As the excitation energy increases, the valley between the peaks of the yield curve rises, suggesting that splitting into two equal fragments, i.e., *symmetric fission*, is becoming more and more probable. At very high energies a single-peak yield curve is observed. Since each fission event produces two fission products, integration under a total fission yield curve gives a total of 200% yield.

The initial or *independent yields* of the fission products of a given A, when plotted versus their Z, fall on a Gaussian curve; the Z at the peak of the curve is referred to as Z_P, i.e., the most probable Z. Wahl *et al.* (227) have shown that a single Gaussian curve will fit the independent yields fairly well for nuclei undergoing fission at low energies (< 6 MeV). In this curve the independent yields, in terms of the fraction of the total chain

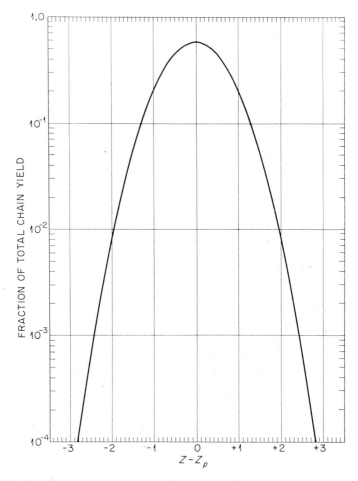

Fig. 27. The independent yield curve. The initial yields of fission products of a given A of all fissioning nuclei lie on this Gaussian curve. The value of Z_P, the most probable Z, does vary with A as well as fissioning nucleus (see Table IV).

yield, is plotted versus a useful function of Z, namely $(Z - Z_P)$. The Z_P value varies depending on the particular A value of the chain as well as on the fissioning nuclide. From the experimental independent yield data, these authors (227) have constructed empirical Z_P vs. A relationships.

Utilizing their data, we have tabulated in Table IV the Z_P values for U^{235} thermal fission for $A = 78$ to $A = 155$.

To summarize, three considerations govern the choice of fission as a way of obtaining a radioisotope. (1) Is the fission cross section large for the target and projectile in question (the cross section for the thermal neutron fission of U^{235} is 582 b.)? (2) Is the total chain yield for the mass of the desired nuclide adequate? Yields as high as 7% are obtained at the peaks of the U^{235} thermal fission curve (Fig. 26). (3) Is the independent yield of the nuclide of interest large enough? Experimentally measured independent yields may be obtained from the compilation of Katcoff (120) or determined from the empirical curve of Wahl et al. (227), using Figure 27 and Table IV. To illustrate the latter procedure, let us consider a specific case:

Should the thermal fission of U^{235} be used to prepare a source of Cs^{136}? First, look at the total fission yield curve, Figure 26; the yield for $A = 136$ is $\sim 6\%$, which is a usefully high value. Now referring to Table IV we see

TABLE IV
EMPIRICAL Z_P VS. A VALUES FOR THE THERMAL FISSION OF U^{235}

A	Z_P	A	Z_P
78	31.0	128	50.2
79	31.3	129	50.3
80	31.6	130	50.4
81	32.0	131	50.8
82	32.3	132	51.3
83	32.7	133	51.5
84	33.1	134	51.8
85	33.5	135	52.4
86	33.9	136	52.6
87	34.4	137	53.3
88	34.9	138	53.4
89	35.4	139	53.8
90	35.8	140	54.3
91	36.3	141	55.0
92	36.8	142	55.4
93	37.4	143	55.9
94	37.8	144	56.4
95	38.4	145	56.8
96	38.2	146	57.2
97	38.65	147	57.7
98	39.1	148	58.1
		149	58.4
		150	58.7

that for $A = 136$, $Z_P = 52.6$; then, since for cesium $Z = 55$ $(Z - Z_P)$ $= +2.4$. Going now to Figure 27, we see that this corresponds to a fractional yield of only 0.2% of the total chain yield. Thus, Cs^{136} would not be formed initially in very great abundance. However, we next check the Chart of the Nuclides (84) to see if any Cs^{136} "grows in" from shorter-lived earlier members of the $A = 136$ chain. Much to our dismay we find that the isobaric neighbor of Cs^{136}, namely, Xe^{136}, is not radioactive and will thus not increase the yield. This "shielded" character of Cs^{136} is fairly uncommon; more frequently, the later members of a chain will increase in yield from the decay of the shorter-lived, earlier members.

Neutrons are also emitted in conjunction with the fission event and these are, of course, essential to sustain a nuclear chain reaction, since they can in turn cause the fission of other nuclei. The energy spectrum of these fission neutrons ranges from a few thousand to several million electron volts with a maximum at about 1 MeV. This makes it feasible to carry out fast-neutron reactions such as (n,p) or (n,α) in a nuclear reactor. Rochlin (195) has reported "effective" cross sections for a number of these reactions in a fission-neutron spectrum.

Heavy nuclei can also be fissioned by particles other than neutrons, and by going to higher and higher incident energies, the fission of lighter nuclei can be observed: Bi^{209} fissions with 22-MeV deuterons and Ta^{181} fissions with 100-MeV O^{16} ions (in this latter case the fissioning species is really Tl^{197}). As mentioned in Section II.2.B, some heavy nuclei such as Cf^{252} possess ground states which lie so close to the fission threshold that the process occurs spontaneously with a half-life that competes with other decay modes.

The intrinsic complexity of the fission process has so far thwarted the numerous attempts at a successful theoretical treatment. The earliest and most frequently explored theoretical approach is that of the liquid-drop model (22). The chief drawback to the liquid-drop approach is that it does not adequately explain asymmetric fission. It has been suggested that certain types of quasi-stationary states of the fissioning nucleus might lead to asymmetric fission (21). A great number of comprehensive reviews and reports of symposia may be consulted for more details of this highly complex subject (27).

B. DEVICES FOR INDUCING NUCLEAR REACTIONS: ACCELERATORS AND
NUCLEAR REACTORS

Although beams of particles for bombardment purposes can be produced from a great variety of apparatus, there are really only two basic types of machines: (1) electrostatic or electromagnetic devices for accelerating charged particles, and (2) chain-reacting devices from which nuclear particles emerge as by-products. The first group is quite varied in design as well as size. The latter category so far includes only neutron-induced fission reactors although a fusion reactor—when one is built—should be usable for fast neutron irradiations.

Charged Particle Accelerators. Although the usual discussion of particle accelerators stresses the device which generates the high voltage, it is only one part of the accelerator system. First, charged particles are generated in an ion source; these ions are then injected into the accelerator proper; finally, the fast-moving ions strike the target. The chemist will generally not be involved in the design of ion source or accelerator. In fact, he may even have little choice of the bombarding particle, since many machines are designed to accelerate a single type; for instance, the Oak Ridge 86-in. cyclotron accelerates only protons. But the chemist should exercise judgment in the choice of target material, and if necessary, design a target assembly to suit his experimental needs.

Ion sources are even more varied than the accelerators they feed (109). However, two types are most common: the *arc type* and the *r.f. type*. The arc ion source consists of a high-voltage arc discharge in an atmosphere consisting of the gas to be ionized. The source proper is a small capsule with a capillary through which the ions are urged by a negatively charged electrode called the *probe*. The r.f. or radio-frequency ion source produces an intense ionized plasma discharge in a glass flask by exposing the gas of interest to a radio-frequency field by coupling the flask to the "tank coil" of a 20–80 megacycle oscillator. Again, a negatively charged probe extracts the ions from the source.

Accelerators either depend on a large electrostatic potential, the "potential-drop" type, or else they accelerate the particles by electronic or electromagnetic means and thus avoid the generation of high voltages. Cockroft-Walton and Van de Graaf accelerators are of the former type. They develop voltages which are applied across evacuated cylinders known as *accelerating tubes*. The greater the charge of the ions introduced at the high-voltage end of the accelerating tube, the more energetic they will be at the target end. The Cockroft-Walton high-voltage set consists of multiple stages of rectification, while the Van de Graaf devices utilize a nonconducting endless belt which carries charge from ground potential to an insulated sphere. The energy ranges for protons accelerated in these two classes of machines are included in the comparison of Figure 28. Recently, the upper limit on the energy attainable with a Van de Graaf has been increased by using two accelerating tubes in "tandem." Negative ions are introduced in the "wrong" end of the first tube and accelerated to the positive end. Then electrons are stripped from the ions and the resulting positive ions are accelerated "down-hill" to the target.

Although the Cockroft-Walton type of accelerator cannot reach very high voltages, its large current capability makes it an excellent fast neutron producer. By bombarding tritium with 100- to 200-keV deuterons, a large yield of 14-MeV neutrons is obtained from the $H^3(d,n)He^4$ reaction. Other reactions with low thresholds, such as $H^2(d,n)He^3$, $Be^9(d,n)Be^{10}$, and $Li^7(p,n)Be^7$, yield abundant quantities of high-energy neutrons. The relative merits of these reactions are discussed in a review by Burrill and MacGregor (34), who also list all the commercially obtainable low-voltage accelerators with comparative performance data.

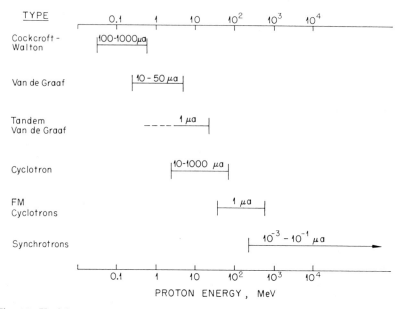

Fig. 28. Useful energy ranges and currents for various types of charged particle accelerators. For comparison, only proton acceleration is considered.

The most common nonpotential drop accelerator is the *cyclotron*. It consists basically of half pancake-shaped hollow electrodes, "dees," hung in a magnetic field. The ions are introduced at the center and spiral outward, receiving a high-frequency kick each time they cross the gap between the two dees. As Figure 26 indicates, cyclotrons have been built with a wide spread in energy capability. To accelerate heavier particles (protons, deuterons) to energies of 100 MeV or more, some variation on the standard cyclotron theme is required. Instead of maintaining a constant radiofrequency, one procedure is to modulate it in a way that will overcome the effect of relativistic mass changes of the fast moving particles. Machines designed in this way are called FM cyclotrons or *synchrocyclotrons*. They cannot accelerate particles continuously, but only in bursts—a few a second; thus, their average ion currents are low, as Figure 28 indicates.

As an alternative to the cyclotron, an accelerator can be constructed with a straight-line configuration consisting of alternate sections of accelerating tubes and gaps. If the sections of "drift" tubes are of the proper length, the particles will arrive at the gaps in time to be accelerated by a microwave oscillator impulse. This type of machine, known as a *linear accelerator*, has been used for the acceleration of protons to $\sim$ 30 MeV and also for electrons to the billion electron volt region. Linear accelerators for the production of beams of heavy ions are in operation at Yale University and Berkeley.

To reach energies of 1 BeV (or 1000 MeV) or more, devices must be used that are similar in operating principle to the FM cyclotrons, except that they also utilize variation of the magnetic field. However, these machines, called *synchrotrons*, are vastly different in appearance from cyclotrons. These huge devices are characterized by race-track-shaped magnets whose diameters vary from 60 feet for the 3-BeV Cosmotron to 800 feet for the 30-BeV Alternating-Gradient accelerator, both of which are located at Brookhaven National Laboratory.

To get a more detailed picture of accelerator design, the interested reader may choose from a variety of well-written treatments; just a few examples are the elementary but excellent book by Wilson and Littauer (238), the brief survey in Friedlander and Kennedy's book (78), or the exhaustive expositions of McMillan (148) and Livingood (140). Howard (108) has compiled a directory of all cyclotrons and high-energy accelerators.

For *target* considerations, the type of accelerator is almost irrelevant. With cyclotrons, targets are often inserted into the vacuum chamber, but with most other accelerators, target assemblies simply are bolted onto a pipe out of which a beam will emerge. Of course, the type and energy of the particles and the beam current are vitally important. Actually, the first consideration is the purpose of the experiment. If one is studying the energy spectra of emitted reaction products, then the target must be extremely thin so that the emergent particles will not suffer energy loss. If one is searching for a new short-lived isotope, the target must be easily and quickly removable from its holder. Subsequent chemical separations should be anticipated so that the target material will be readily soluble. The target should be only slightly larger than the beam so that laborious dissolution of unactivated material can be avoided. Once the chemical requirements are satisfied by a proper choice of target material, two other factors govern the target design: mechanical retention and cooling. Obviously, the target must be tied down, but it may be done in a variety of ways. Metals are easiest: foils may be bolted to a backing or preferably electroplated onto a more inert base plate (cf., Fig. 29). Powdered material must be enclosed but the covering material should be of minimum thickness. Two different powder targets are shown in Figure 29. The "hat" type is the simpler,

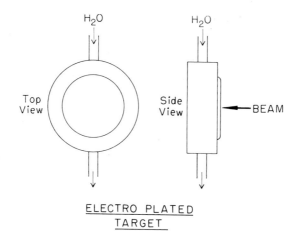

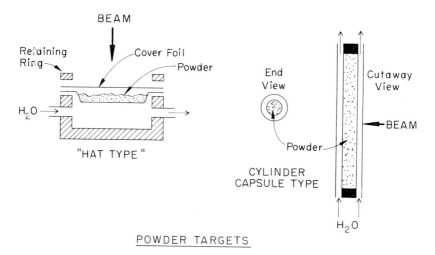

Fig. 29. Typical accelerator targets. Water is indicated as the coolant; however, other substances may be used.

easier to fabricate, and can be opened more quickly. The capsule type, consisting of a double-walled cylinder with the coolant circulating through the annular space, can dissipate more heat, hence tolerate higher currents.

This type of target was designed for use with the Oak Ridge 86-in. cyclotron which produces internal beams of > 1 ma. (146, 147).

That target cooling is needed is graphically illustrated by calculating the power delivered by a charged particle beam: a 100-μa. beam of 100-MeV protons produces 10 kw. Needless to say, this heat must be dissipated or the target will be vaporized. The targets of Figure 29 are all provided with coolant pipes. Water is the most commonly used coolant, although for low absorption targets (with small beam currents) gas cooling is used. The basic axiom of cooling is to provide as high a coolant flow as is mechanically feasible. If there is no limitation on target size, the target may be placed at an angle to the emergent beam, spreading it across a larger area, and thus minimizing the heat dissipation problem (147). Rotating targets have also been used for the same purpose. Trouble may be encountered if the beam is allowed to penetrate into the cooling water. Radiolysis of the water frequently leads to extensive corrosion of the cooling system plumbing.

Neutronic Chain Reactors or Nuclear Reactors. Bombardment facilities at nuclear reactors have become widely available in recent years. All but a few nuclear reactors utilize the thermal-neutron fission of U^{235}. Some reactors use the fast neutron fission of U^{235} and several substitute Pu^{239} as fuel.

Thermal-neutron reactors consist of five basic components:

1. *The nuclear fuel.* A sufficient amount (referred to as the critical mass) of fissionable material must be used to sustain the chain reaction. Such a chain reaction is feasible since fission is accompanied by emission of neutrons which can in turn cause fission in other nuclei. The fissionable material is arranged in some sort of a matrix, called the *reactor core.*

2. *A neutron-moderating material.* The cross section for the fission of U^{235} is very high for thermal neutrons but drops precipitously for higher energy neutrons. Hence, to keep the critical size small the energetic neutrons emitted in fission must be slowed down. The best moderators are light elements, e.g., hydrogen (H_2O or D_2O are its most convenient forms) or carbon.

3. *A control system.* The operation of a reactor is begun by removing from the core a piece of neutron-absorbing material (cadmium, for example); this object is referred to as the *control rod.* By actuating a motor-driven control rod with signals from a radiation detector, the reactor operation can be made automatic.

4. *Heat removal.* The tremendous energy release accompanying the fission process is manifested as heat. To prevent the melting down (or boiling away) of the core, this heat must be dissipated, or in the case of power reactors, used to generate electricity.

5. *Shielding.* Since nuclear reactors produce lethal quantities of neutrons, beta rays, and gamma rays, they must be shielded with large masses of concrete or deep pools of water.

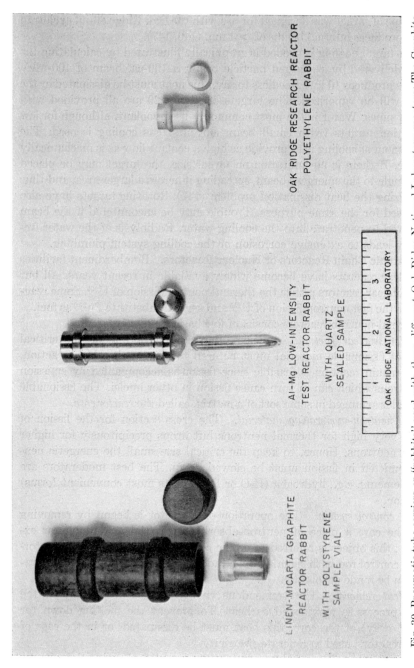

Fig. 30. Pneumatic tube carriers or "rabbits" used with three different Oak Ridge National Laboratory reactors: The Graphite Reactor, the Low-Intensity Test Reactor, and the Oak Ridge Research Reactor. Also shown are two examples of sample containment within rabbits. Quartz wool used for padding is seen at the opening of the Al-Mg rabbit.

The historic first reactor at the University of Chicago consisted of a matrix of natural uranium fuel and graphite moderator. Research reactors of this type are still in operation at Oak Ridge, Brookhaven, and Harwell, and gas-cooled graphite reactors designed for power production have been built, particularly in the United Kingdom. These reactors are notable for their large external size, e.g., the active volume of the Oak Ridge graphite reactor is a 24-ft. cube.

By utilizing enriched U^{235} a much smaller critical size can be attained. Both *heterogeneous* and *homogeneous* enriched uranium research reactors have been built. The heterogeneous reactors consist of metallic fuel plates suspended in H_2O (or D_2O), which serves both as coolant and moderator. The core may be contained in a small tank, in which case the water is force-circulated through the core tank and then through heat exchangers. Examples of this type of reactor are the Materials Testing Reactor (MTR) at Reactor Testing Station, Idaho, the Low Intensity Test Reactor (LITR) at Oak Ridge, the Oak Ridge Research Reactor (ORR), the Argonne Research Reactor (CP-5), the Harwell Heavy Water Reactor (E-443) and the Chalk River Reactor (NRX). Alternatively, the fuel element array is hung in a pool and convective cooling is utilized ("swimming pool" reactor). The prototypic homogeneous reactor—the Los Alamos "water boiler" reactor—consisted of about 4 kg. of 15% enriched U^{235} dissolved in dilute H_2SO_4 and contained in a 1-ft. diameter stainless steel sphere. Detailed descriptions of several specific research reactors, as well as complete listings of all nuclear reactors, are to be found in several recently published surveys (6).

Neutron beams emerging from reactors are extremely useful for elaborate studies such as neutron diffraction measurements of crystal structure. However, the flux in such beams is 10^4 or so times smaller than the flux in the reactor core. Thus, for purposes of producing tracer nuclides, samples are always placed in or near the core. Samples can be manually inserted into access holes in reactors; however, the radiation emerging from such openings when a reactor is in operation prevents such a procedure. An exception is the swimming pool reactor; target material suspended from a string can be lowered at any time into the region of high neutron flux.

Pneumatic tubes similar to those used in department stores are installed in most research reactors. These provide rapid and, if necessary, automatic conveyance of samples in and out of reactor cores. The wide variation in these facilities is exemplified by Figure 30, which depicts the carriers or "rabbits" used with three different pneumatic tubes at three Oak Ridge reactors. The linen-micarta rabbit is suitable for long bombardments in the graphite reactor since the ambient temperature is only 60°C.; the plastic vial which is shown is adequate as a disposable sample container.

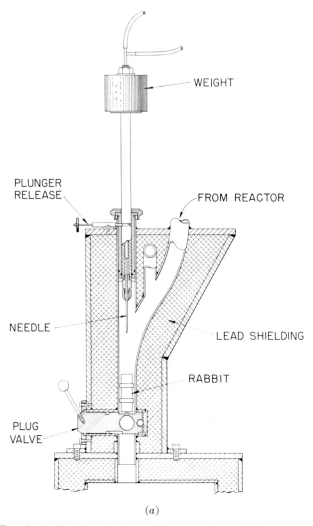

(a)

Fig. 31. The solution-handling device used in conjunction with the pneumatic tube of the Oak Ridge Graphite Reactor. (a) A cutaway view of the pneumatic-tube terminus. (b) Detailed view of solution rabbit and transfer needle.

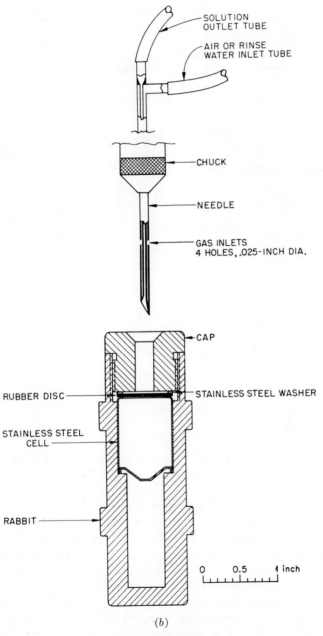

SOLUTION OUTLET TUBE

AIR OR RINSE WATER INLET TUBE

CHUCK

NEEDLE

GAS INLETS 4 HOLES, .025-INCH DIA.

CAP

RUBBER DISC

STAINLESS STEEL WASHER

STAINLESS STEEL CELL

RABBIT

0   0.5   1 inch

(b)

Fig. 31 (continued).

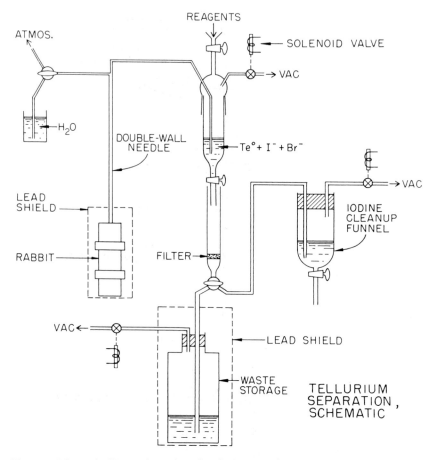

Fig. 32. Schematic illustration of a chemical separation system using the solution-handling device of Figure 31.

Long bombardments in high-temperature and high-flux reactors, such as the LITR or ORR, require the use of metal rabbits and the sealing of samples in quartz ampoules. However, such metal rabbits become highly activated and must be stored for several days before sample removal. If one is interested in a short-lived isotope, he needs to obtain it soon after the end of the bombardment. Then a plastic rabbit should be used such as the polyethylene ORR rabbit shown in Figure 30. For bombardment times of less than five minutes, decomposition or melting of the polyethylene rabbits does not occur and activation is minimal. Samples are either sealed in small pieces of polyethylene tubing or else placed directly in the rabbit.

For short-lived isotope work, bombardment of solutions is advantageous. Pneumatic tubes equipped with solution-handling devices permit remote removal of the irradiated solution within a few seconds. The arrangement used with the Oak Ridge Graphite Reactor is shown in Figure 31. Figure 31a is a cutaway view of the pneumatic-tube terminus with the rabbit in position and the hypodermic transfer needle poised above, and in Figure 31b a close-up of the internal details of the solution rabbit and needle is given. The solution is contained in the stainless steel cell which is sealed with a rubber disk.

A schematic representation of a specific use of this apparatus is given in Figure 32. In this experiment I^{134} was separated from the fission products of U^{235} (114). In order to discriminate against other iodine nuclides a rapid tellurium separation was first performed and the I^{134} was allowed to grow in from the decay of Te^{134}. The irradiated uranium solution was transferred out of the rabbit by suction and discharged into the first separatory funnel, where the tellurium separation was performed. The Te precipitate was quickly filtered and the bulk of the radioactivity drained into a shielded waste container. The Te was dissolved and the solution transferred to the next separatory funnel where subsequent iodine extractions were performed.

The precautions to be taken in preparing a sample for bombardment depend, of course, on the length of irradiation and the ambient temperature of the reactor. Solutions and volatile targets can only receive short bombardments in high-temperature reactors. For long bombardments, samples should be sealed preferably in a vitreous material such as quartz which activates much less than glass; further, several forms of glass contain boron in sufficient concentration to materially reduce the neutron flux. The capsule wall strength should be such as to contain the pressure equivalent to the volatilization of the entire sample. If a quartz-enclosed sample is pneumatically injected, it should be packed into the rabbit with quartz wool to prevent breakage.

V. SEPARATION TECHNIQUES*

Other sections of this volume have alluded to chemical separations of radioactive tracers. How do these processes differ from conventional analytical procedures? We will in this section discuss these differences as well as those experimental considerations which govern the choice of a par-

* In addition to the general references listed earlier, the reviews of Finston and Miskel (73) and Stevenson and Hicks (216) may be consulted for general discussions of chemical separations.

ticular separation method. Finally, we will mention briefly the currently important types of separation methods.

1. Unique Aspects of Tracer Separations

A. ISOTOPE EFFECT

Although the usual basic assumption is that a tracer atom behaves chemically exactly as nonradioactive isotopes with the same atomic number, rates of reactions may be different for atoms of a different mass. Only when the relative mass difference is large, does this *isotope effect* become significant. In experiments with tritium, reaction rates differ by factors of 2 or 3 from those for "ordinary" hydrogen. With C^{14} as a tracer, differences in reaction rates are never greater than about 7%. Generally, such isotope effects only occur in processes involving bond rupture or formation (15).

B. LOW CONCENTRATION EFFECTS

To emphasize the tremendous degree of dilution of a tracer solution, let us calculate the concentration of Co^{II} ions in 1 ml. of a Co^{60} solution in which 10^3 disintegrations/sec.-ml. are occurring.

$$A = \lambda N = 10^3$$

$$= \frac{0.693}{5.2 \text{ yr.} \times 3.2 \times 10^7 \text{ sec./yr.}} \times N$$

$$N = 2.4 \times 10^{11} \text{ atoms/ml.}$$

This corresponds to a Co^{II} concentration of $4 \times 10^{-10}M$. With such extremely low concentrations, peculiar chemical phenomena can be expected. First of all, under certain conditions, minute particles of "junk," which are present in even multiply distilled H_2O, contain sufficient adsorption sites to seize all the tracer ions present. Likewise, the radioactive atoms may adhere to the vessel walls and various other interfaces. It is even possible to centrifuge out the radioactivity if these adsorptive conditions are operative. This behavior became known as "radio-colloid behavior" in the period preceding World War II when it seemed to be an intrinsic property of certain radioisotopes.

Certain equilibria which under macro conditions lie far in one direction may shift to the opposite side at tracer levels. For instance, I_2 in extremely dilute solutions becomes unstable:

$$I_2 + H_2O = H^+ + I^- + HIO$$

Rates and mechanisms of reactions involving tracer atoms may be drastically different than at normal concentrations. For example, the rate-determining step of a reaction at macro concentrations might involve the collision of two molecules of reactant A. On a carrier-free level such a path would be unobservable, since the colliding of two tracer atoms would be highly improbable. This effect permits the dominance of reaction paths that are of negligible importance at macro concentrations.

Low concentration effects are troublesome in most chemical separations and details of some of these difficulties will be cited in connection with specific types of separations in Part 3 of this section. Of course these problems can be avoided by adding to the tracer solution a macro amount of the stable isotope of the same element. The tracer will then be "carried along" with the bulk quantity of stable isotope in all chemical manipulations. Hence, this is referred to as adding "carrier" to the solution. Conversely, a radioisotope solution to which no stable isotope has been added is called "carrier-free."

The assumption that an added carrier will "do its job" is a potentially dangerous one. Because of chemical excitation resulting from the nuclear processes, the tracer may be in an unexpected chemical state; hence, a complete mixing or exchange between the carrier and tracer may not occur. This phenomenon will be treated in Part 1.C. and techniques for ensuring consistent behavior will be described.

C. CHEMICAL EFFECTS OF NUCLEAR TRANSFORMATIONS

We have just suggested that it is dangerous to produce a tracer by a nuclear reaction or radioactive decay and then to assume that the tracer's chemical state is predictable on the basis of everyday non-nuclear experience. Just how badly deceived one can be is best illustrated by a few hyyothetical case histories.

Some Typical Effects. Chemist A, planning to study properties of the PO_4^{-3} ion, produces P^{32} through the reaction Cl^{35} $(n,\alpha)P^{32}$ by irradiating NaCl with fast neutrons. After irradiation he dissolves the crystals and adds PO_4^{-3} carrier. Succeeding chemical steps begin to show anomalous effects as if all the radioactivity were not present as PO_4^{-3}. It has been shown that P^{32} produced in this manner may be present in the -3, $+1$, $+3$ oxidation states as well as the $+5$ (39).

Chemist B bombards a solution of U^{235} in a nuclear reactor hoping to extract the 53-min. I^{134} to use in a study of the solubility of AgI. He adds 10 mg. of I^- carrier, and NO_2^- solution to oxidize the I^- to I_2. Extracting with CCl_4 produces the characteristic purple-colored organic phase. However, when he checks the organic phase for radioactivity, he finds only a small amount has extracted and that the majority of the I^{134} has remained in the aqueous phase. It has been found that fission product iodine is present in a variety of oxidation states (88). In the case cited above, most of the

I^{134} was probably in oxidized forms such as IO_3^- or IO_4^- and thus was unaffected by the nitrite oxidation and subsequent extraction.

Chemist C, with an interest in gas kinetics, wants some tagged methyl iodide. He seals ordinary gaseous methyl iodide in a small vial and irradiates it in a nuclear reactor to produce CH_3I^{128} by I^{127} (n,γ). After the bombardment and routine gas purification treatment, he is dismayed to find almost no radioactive iodine in his methyl iodide, although the emptied vial and the gas scrubbers do contain abundant amounts of I^{128}. The breaking of bonds of organic halide compounds as a consequence of a neutron-capture reaction was one of the earliest observations of this peculiar phenomenon, which became known as the "hot-atom effect" (220).

We will now explore the causes of these phenomena by first discussing the mechanisms which initially excite the tracer atoms. Then we will examine the influences of the medium in which they are produced and the effect of background radiation. Finally, practical details for circumventing these difficulties will be given.

Excitation Modes. That spectacular chemical changes occur as a consequence of nuclear transformations is not surprising when one examines the primary effects which they produce. Considerable momentum may be imparted to a target nucleus undergoing a nuclear reaction. In fact, if the target is quite thin and the bombarding energy high enough, the product nucleus may recoil completely out of the target. Since in most radioisotope production bombardments, thick targets will be used to maximize yield, recoil loss of product is negligible. However, the recoiling atom will possess sufficient velocity to strip off a number of its electrons. Further, if the nuclear transformation involves a change in the charge of the nucleus, e.g., (p,n), (n,p), or β^- decay, the orbital electrons will be excited by the sudden increase or decrease in the central field and again loss of extra-nuclear electrons will occur. Finally, the two processes most effective in causing ionization are radioactive decay by orbital electron capture and the emission of internal conversion electrons (see Section II.2.D). Both of these latter processes produce holes in the innermost electron orbitals which initiate emission of Auger electrons. Ions with charges as high as 20+ have been observed following conversion electron emission in Xe^{131} (180). Fragments resulting from heavy-element nuclear fission also emerge with extremely large charges.

The first event in the life of these highly charged, frequently fast-moving ions is their breaking away from their parent molecule, crystal, surface, or other affiliation. Then, recoiling through the medium, they produce a dense track of ions and radicals and ultimately may react again to form in some cases the parent molecule. Frequently, new species result which cannot be synthesized at room temperature.

Other Factors. Two factors seem to be dominant in determining the ultimate fate of these excited atoms. First, the physical state of the system is of prime importance in determining the ability of the charged ions to recombine to produce the parent species or a new species. Second, the presence of *background radiation* has quite an effect. Bombardment in a nuclear reactor or a charged particle accelerator exposes the sample to a huge flux of background radiation (gamma rays, etc.) which produces a high concentration of ion pairs and free radicals by radiolysis. These very reactant species strongly influence the reactions of the ions resulting from the nuclear transformation. When the tracer atom of interest results from radioactive decay, the flux of background radiation is extremely low, namely, that due to beta and gamma rays accompanying the decay. Hence, the only ion pairs or radicals entering the picture will be those produced by the recoiling ion itself. As a consequence, the radioactive yields of the various species show sharp differences depending on the origin of the radionuclides. Let us cite an example: if $KBrO_3$ is exposed to neutrons in a reactor, about 20% of the radioactive Br^{80} that is formed is present as BrO_3^- and the remainder in lower oxidation states. On the other hand, if $KBrO_3$ tagged with Br^{80m} (which decays by conversion electron emission to Br^{80}) is allowed to decay, the yield of Br^{80} tagged BrO_3^- increases to $\sim 35\%$ (100).

An extremely large amount of effort has been expended studying these effects. A recent international conference on the subject summarized the current status of this perplexingly varied field (219), and its proceedings as well as earlier review articles (236) may be consulted by the curious reader. From the point of view of this treatment, a more concise picture is needed. With this in mind we have listed in Table V the general effects expected for "targets" in different initial states. Here, the term "target" refers to the substance in which the tracer-producing process—(n,p) reaction or beta decay, for example—has occurred. Where Table V indicates a variety of products, actually only the relatively stable oxidation states or molecular forms will be observed. Thus, Na^{+2}, if produced initially, will be rapidly reduced. In addition, rapidly exchanging states will not coexist. For example, if the tracer is in the Br^0 state and Br^{-1} carrier is added, an extremely rapid electron transfer exchange will occur and the radioactivity will only be observed in the -1 state.

Ways of Avoiding the Effects. Enough of diagnosing the illness; let us now discuss the cure. For most inorganic radiochemical separations, the problem is one of multiple oxidation states. The best way to avoid this difficulty is to add carrier and cycle it through all the oxidation states with appropriate oxidizing and reducing agents. As an example, let us recall the dilemma of Chemist B described above; the following procedure pro-

TABLE V
DEPENDENCE OF THE CHEMICAL EFFECTS OF NUCLEAR TRANSFORMATIONS ON
TARGET STATE

Target state	Effect
Gas	Little recombination or reaction; hence, almost always smaller fragments of parent molecule result. *Diatomic Molecules.* Recombination may occur due to instability of monoatoms.
Liquid	Recombination and reaction with radicals are important and many species (even polymeric forms) result. *Solutions* Non-ionic Solute. Similar to liquid pure compounds, except that radicals and ion pairs in the solvent become dominant. Ionic Solute. A variety of oxidation states may be produced.
Solid	Recoiling ions may be trapped interstitially, but usually some "annealing" of electronic damage will occur. *Conducting Solids.* All electronic damage will anneal and the "normal" oxidation state will be observed upon dissolution. *Non-ionic Solids.* Effects seem to be similar to those in liquids, suggesting the recoiling atom "melts" a tiny segment of the solid. *Ionic Crystals.* Although considerable self-annealing occurs, many ions are trapped interstitially and then react on dissolution to produce a variety of oxidation states. (Under radiation some solid targets undergo transitions to crystal states that are difficult to dissolve.)

duces good exchange of carrier iodine with fission product iodine: I^- is added and oxidized with alkaline hypochlorite, then reduced with bisulfite, and finally oxidized with nitrite. Most compiled separation procedures detail precautionary steps to ensure good tracer and carrier exchange.

As for non-ionic substances, most bond rupture effects are nonreversible. The best procedure is to produce the tracer in a simple state and then synthesize the tagged form. Alternatively, one might start with a more complex molecule which fragments into the desired species.

Preparation of High Specific Activity Sources. As mentioned earlier in this discussion, this phenomenon of bond rupture in organic halogen molecules is of historical interest. It was utilized in a practical way by Szilard and Chalmers (220) to remove the radioactive I^{128} from the bulk of inactive target material, ethyl iodide. The exploitation of this phenomenon to produce high specific-activity tracers has become known as the *Szilard-Chalmers effect.*

Another method for "enriching" the reaction products makes use of the fact that target nuclei may recoil completely out of very thin targets. The recoiling ions can be trapped directly in "catcher foils" or brought to rest in an inert gas and then collected by electrostatic methods (101). In a recently developed method, the recoil particles are stopped in a fast-moving gas stream and then swept several feet to a filter on which they are collected (79).

D. THE SCALE OF TRACER SEPARATIONS

In general, separations involving radionuclides are performed on a semi-micro scale; typically 1–100 mg. of carrier are used. In a few very special cases, such as the discovery of "synthetic elements," micro and ultramicro techniques are required.

Modifications of conventional analytical procedures and apparatus are sometimes necessary in cases requiring remote handling or very rapid processing. The final step of the procedure is designed to prepare the sample for counting. Details of the "source-mounting" techniques will be given in Section VII.

E. QUANTITATIVE SEPARATION NOT NEEDED

For most purposes, separations of tracer materials need not be quantitative. On the other hand, scrupulous purity of the product usually must be maintained. These seemingly contradictory requirements can be justified from the viewpoint of the specific separation motive. First and foremost, the experimenter wants to exclude impurities which would carry along radioactive nuclides whose radiations might be confused with those of the nuclide of interest. It is true that impurities which introduce no radioactive interference or contamination can usually be tolerated. The degree of separation from impurities is usually referred to in terms of the *decontamination factor*, which is the fraction of the undesirable impurity present after separation. The required decontamination factor will depend on the decay properties of the impurity nuclides and the intended use of the tracer.

To insure adequate decontamination it is sometimes necessary to perform certain procedural steps repeatedly, even though this may result in some loss of product. In cases requiring precise knowledge of the degree of quantitativeness or *chemical yield*, a known amount of carrier can be added to begin the separation. Then as the final step the quantity of surviving carrier is redetermined. From these two quantities the chemical yield can be computed.

2. Strategy of a Separation

Planning is even more important for tracer separations than for most analytical procedures. First of all, a chemist may be dealing with a very short-lived isotope. He would not have time to deliberate or reconsider while carrying out the procedure. Further, if his separation were to fail, he could not go to the shelf, open a bottle, and pour out a new sample; generally a new bombardment involving expense of more time and money would be required. A procedure should be carefully chosen and then tested and rehearsed using natural material or long-lived tracers. Three criteria govern the choice of a specific separation procedure; the time available, the mode of formation of the tracer, and the ultimate use of the tracer. Ideally, the time for a separation should be only a small fraction of the half-life of the desired nuclide. To study very short-lived isotopes ($t_{1/2}$ $\sim$ 10 min., for example), rapidly equilibrating processes such as solvent extraction should be chosen instead of slow operations like homogeneous precipitation.

In some nuclear reactions only a single radioactive species is produced, in others two or three processes compete, and in some reactions, such as nuclear fission, a broad spectrum of products result (cf., Section IV.). Obviously, the separation should be designed to remove the desired element from those impurity radioactivities that are expected. If only a few contaminants are present, the first step can be a specific one. On the other hand, when a myriad of unwanted species have resulted, then an initial rough separation must usually be performed, followed by further purification steps.

The ultimate use of the tracer will bear heavily on the initial and final stages of the separation. Whether carrier is added or not will depend on the experiment in which it will be used. For absolute determination of disintegration rate, for example, a massless (carrier-free) source is desired; if it is necessary to know the chemical yield, one must add stable carrier. Finally, if the tracer is to be used exclusively in solution, it would be a pointless last step to precipitate the tracer; however, if a source were to be mounted on a plate for counting, slurrying a precipitate would be a handy technique (Section VII).

3. Separation Procedures

Accompanying the growth in the use and study of radioisotopes has been an increase in the number and variety of separation methods. The first large summary of procedures was in *Radiochemical Studies: The Fission Products* (49) which included most of the methods from the wartime Manhattan Project. Since then, various compilations from individual laboratories have emerged (149). To bring order to this mass of information and to provide a clearinghouse for new procedures, the Subcommittee on Radiochemistry of the National Academy of Sciences is sponsoring the publication of a series of monographs on the "Radiochemistry of the Ele-

VI. DETECTION AND MEASUREMENT OF NUCLEAR RADIATION

In recent years the technique of radiation characterization has undergone a rapid transformation. New materials of construction have made possible a number of improvements in conventional detectors, while a host of new detector types have been made available to the experimenter.

For the purpose of the discussion to follow, it will be convenient to consider a radiation detection system in two parts. The first of these is the detector, in which the radiation interacts; the complementary part is the measuring apparatus, which is designed to receive the information from the detector and to present in convenient form such data as radiation type, intensity, and energy spectrum.

The most common detectors make use of one of the two main processes by which radiation transfers energy to a stopping material, i.e., excitation and ionization (see Section III). In the detectors to be discussed, molecular dissociation is of small importance; however, this effect is the basis of the chemical dosimeters which find important applications in health physics.

One of the most useful and versatile detectors now in use is the scintillation counter, which uses the fluorescent light emitted when charged particles pass through certain stopping materials. The basic process here is excitation, although the interaction of the stopping medium with the incident particle may involve ionization and molecular dissociation as well.

Several types of radiation detectors make use of the ionization produced by the passage of charged particles. This class of detector includes ionization chambers, proportional counters, Geiger counters, and semiconductor radiation detectors. If the incident radiation consists of charged particles such as alpha particles or electrons, the ionization is produced directly (primary ionization); however, uncharged species such as gamma rays or neutrons must first interact with the detector to produce charged particles, and the ionization in this case is a secondary process.

Improvements in detectors have been accompanied by the development of more versatile and reliable electronic measuring equipment. Where once it was possible to record only the number of events in a certain detector, it is now quite common to record complicated spectral data. Many of the new techniques in nuclear data processing were inspired by progress in digital computer technology; this has resulted in a very desirable compatibility between modern nuclear equipment and digital computers. Hence, information from a radiation detection system now may be recorded and processed in a highly automated manner.

Limitations of space restrict the following discussion to a brief treatment of detection systems which are most important to the chemist utilizing radioactivity. Particular emphasis will be given to some of the new methods, such as scintillation counting and the use of semiconductor radiation detectors. It is suggested that the reader consult the various reviews (48, 74, 117, 132, 181, 198, 206, 210, 212, 232) for a more detailed description of the principles and applications of detection techniques than is included here.

1. Scintillation Techniques*

A. INTRODUCTION

One of the earliest techniques for detection of charged particles involved counting the scintillations produced in a phosphor screen. Such a device was employed by Rutherford and his collaborators in their famous study of alpha-particle scattering by nuclei. The scintillation method eventually gave way to electrical counters, which were more reliable and capable of functioning at high rates.

Modern scintillation counters followed closely the development of high-gain photomultiplier tubes. Combining various scintillating materials with a photomultiplier to count the scintillations has resulted in the most versatile detector available for nuclear research.

Present-day scintillation counters possess a number of advantages over gas counters: They not only indicate the presence of a particle, but also may be used to record rate of energy loss, or the energy if the scintillator is thick enough. With the proper combination of scintillator and photomultiplier tube, the detector is ideally suited to high counting-rate applications. The high density of solid or liquid scintillators has made the scintillation counter the most efficient gamma-ray detector available.

A functional diagram of a scintillation detector is shown in Figure 33. The energy of the incident radiation is converted to light in the scintillator. The reflector and optical coupling insure that this light is transmitted efficiently to the photocathode, where the light energy is converted to a burst of photoelectrons. An electrostatic focusing electrode collects the photoelectrons and focuses them on the electron multiplier structure.

The electron multiplier increases the number of electrons by secondary electron emission from a cascade of elements called *dynodes*. The multiplication of a typical dynode is about 4; hence, the over-all current gain for the standard, 10-stage multiplier is $(4)^{10}$, or about 10^6. A variety of 10-stage photomultiplier tubes are available, with over-all gains of $(0.6–5.0) \times 10^6$.

When a burst of electrons arrives at the anode, the current which flows

---

* For general references on scintillation detectors and applications, see Bell (8), Crouthamel (51), Mott and Sutton (160), Murray (161), and O'Kelley (163).

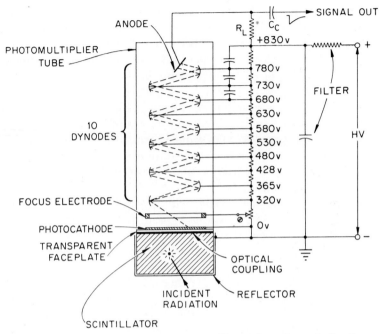

Fig. 33. Diagram of a scintillation counter, illustrating schematically the way in which light from the scintillator is coupled to a photomultiplier tube. A typical wiring diagram is shown for the 10-stage photomultiplier operated with a positive high-voltage supply.

through R_L yields a voltage drop which is coupled to the measuring equipment through the blocking capacitor C_c. This negative output pulse will generally have an amplitude of a few millivolts to perhaps a few volts. The rise time of the pulse—that is, the time for the pulse to rise from 10% to 90% of its maximum height—is determined by the lifetime of the excited state in the scintillator which emits the light, and by the time spread introduced by the multiplier. The time for the signal pulse to return to zero is determined by the product of the net anode load resistance (R_L in parallel with the input resistance of the amplifier) and the capacitance of the signal lead to ground.

B. ELECTRON DETECTION AND SPECTROMETRY

The scintillation method is very well suited to the detection of electrons. This subject will be considered at the outset, not only because of its intrinsic interest, but also as a necessary preliminary to a discussion of gamma-ray detection, in which photons are detected by the secondary electrons produced.

Scintillators. Organic scintillators are best for spectrometry and counting of electrons and beta distributions, largely because of their low effective atomic number. A low atomic number reduces the probability of *backscattering*, in which an electron incident on a scintillator may scatter out, leaving only a fraction of its original energy in the scintillator. This effect is worse at low energies and for high atomic number scintillators. The organic scintillators have an additional advantage in that their gamma-ray sensitivity is low, so beta particles may be counted in the presence of moderate gamma-ray fields. To reduce gamma-ray interference, the minimum thickness of scintillator required for electron detection should be used. Further remarks on scattering and correction for gamma-ray background will be found below.

It is convenient to divide organic scintillators into two classes: single crystals and solutions. Anthracene is typical of the single crystals, and because of its early popularity in the formative years of scintillation spectroscopy, it has become the standard against which other scintillators are usually compared. Characteristics of anthracene and a number of other typical organic scintillators are shown in Table VI. It will be seen that although anthracene yields the largest light output of any organic scintillator, its fluorescence decay is the slowest listed; therefore, applications which demand very rapid pulse rise times may require a scintillator with faster response at a sacrifice in pulse height.

Although much useful work has been performed using scintillating crystals, the development of liquid and solid (plastic) solution scintillators has endowed scintillation counting with new scope. The liquid scintillators have the advantage of easy fabrication in almost unlimited volumes.

TABLE VI
ORGANIC CRYSTAL SCINTILLATORS[a]

Material	Density, g./cm.³	Relative pulse height for β excitation	Time for decay to $1/e$ of initial light intensity, nsec.[b]	Wavelength of maximum emission, A.
Anthracene	1.25	100	23 to 38	4450
trans-Stilbene	1.16	46	<3 to 8.2	3850
p-Terphenyl	1.23	30	4.5	4000
p-Quaterphenyl	—	94	4.2	4350

[a] From the compilation by W. E. Mott and R. B. Sutton, in S. Flügge and E. Creutz, eds., *Handbuch der Physik–Encyclopedia of Physics*, Vol. XLV, Springer, Berlin, 1958; references to specific authors are given by Mott and Sutton.
[b] One nsec. = 10^{-9} sec.

Plastic scintillators are mechanically rugged and can be readily machined. Both liquid and plastic solutions can be obtained with fluorescence lifetimes as short as the best crystalline scintillators. Some examples of solution scintillators will be found in Table VII.

TABLE VII
ORGANIC SOLUTION SCINTILLATORS[a]

Solvent	Primary solute,[b] g./liter	Secondary solute,[b] g./liter	Relative pulse height[c]	Wavelength of maximum emission, A.
Toluene	PPO(4)[d]	POPOP(0.1)	61	—
Toluene	TP(4)	POPOP(0.1)	61	4320
Polyvinyltoluene	TP(36)	POPOP(1)	51	4300
Polyvinyltoluene	TP(36)	DPS(0.9)	52	3800

[a] From F. N. Hayes, D. G. Ott, and V. N. Kerr, *Nucleonics*, **14**, No. 1, 42 (1956).
[b] Solute abbreviations: PPO = 2,5-diphenyloxazole; TP = *p*-terphenyl; POPOP = 1,4-di(2-(5-phenyloxazolyl))-benzene; DPS = *p-p'*-diphenylstilbene.
[c] Pulse height for electron excitation, relative to anthracene pulse height as 100.
[d] PPO is preferred for low-temperature applications because of the poor solubility of TP in cold toluene.

Solution scintillators may be made from two, or more often three, components. The bulk material is the solvent, in which a scintillating substance termed the *primary solute* is dissolved; another scintillator called the *secondary solute* or *wavelength shifter* is usually included. It is generally accepted that the incident particle first dissipates its energy by producing ionized and excited molecules of the solvent, and free electrons. Then, most of the energy is transferred by nonradiative processes to the primary solute. The amount of energy so transferred depends on the overlap between the emission spectrum of the solvent and the absorption spectrum of the primary solute.

Many of the primary solutes which may be used with the common hydrocarbon solvents fluoresce at such a short wavelength that a conventional photomultiplier tube cannot efficiently make use of the light; for this reason, the secondary solute is added to the solution. The absorption band of this latter solute should overlap the emission band of the primary solute. The final emission should be shifted to a longer wavelength which falls within the photomultiplier response and for which the absorption of light by the solution is small.

The solute concentration in solution scintillators is rather low. As can be seen in Table VII, the primary solute concentration ranges from a few per cent for plastics down to less than one per cent for liquids. The required

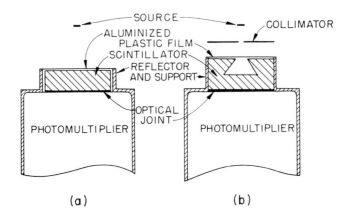

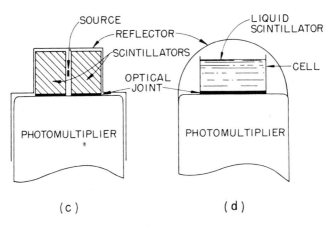

Fig. 34. Mounting arrangements for electron detectors using organic scintillators. (*a*) Flat scintillator. (*b*) "Hollow-crystal" spectrometer, with electrons collimated into a well. (*c*) "Split-crystal" spectrometer, in which the electron source is sandwiched between two scintillators. (*d*) A counter using a liquid scintillator, in which the beta emitter is dissolved.

concentration of secondary solute is only a few per cent of that of the primary.

It is a familiar and often distressing fact that the addition of certain impurities to liquid scintillators, even in small concentrations, decreases the light output enormously. Clearly, any additive which interferes with the energy transfer sequence will tend to quench the fluorescence. Such quenching will occur if the foreign substance has an absorption band at the emission wavelength for the solvent or one of the solutes and if the energy thus transmitted is dissipated by processes which do not give rise to useful light. The mechanism of quenching has been under study for some time in several laboratories, and has been discussed in a number of review articles (18, 32, 118).

The choice of a solvent for a solution scintillator depends upon the application. For liquid solutions xylene is usually preferred, because it yields the greatest pulse height for a particular primary solute. On the other hand, toluene exhibits a much smaller absorption of the fluorescent light, and is recommended where large volumes are required. Also, toluene does not react with some of the common light reflectors used in scintillation counters to the extent that xylene does. Other solvents are used in cases where it is necessary to introduce materials which are insoluble in toluene or xylene. For example, water is only slightly soluble in the usual scintillator solution, and has a strong quenching effect; aqueous solutions can be introduced by using p-dioxane as the solvent, and reducing the quenching effect with naphthalene. The details of liquid scintillator preparation, together with applications to various problems, will be found in several reviews (7, 103).

Except for the fact that they are solid solutions, the composition and fluorescence properties of plastic scintillators are similar to those of liquid scintillators. The only important base plastics (solvents) in use are polystyrene and polyvinyltoluene; some examples are given in Table VII. From the standpoint of convenience in machining and polishing, a plastic is to be preferred over anthracene; however, it should be borne in mind that the pulse height from a plastic is only about half that of anthracene, which leads to poorer resolution in electron spectroscopy. In counting applications and in spectroscopy at high electron energies, the plastics are to be highly recommended because of their convenience.

Detector Arrangements. Several ways in which organic scintillators may be used are sketched in Figure 34. In Figure 34a is shown the simplest arrangement, a cylindrical crystal optically coupled to a photomultiplier tube. While this detector may be used for counting beta particles or electrons, it is not suitable for measurement of low-energy spectra because of the backscattering effect already described. Above about 1.5 MeV the backscattering probability is reduced to a point such that beta-ray spectra can be determined accurately with this simple detector, if the shape of the low-energy part of the spectrum is of no concern.

The scattering problem can be circumvented in a number of ways. A helpful technique is to collimate the electron beam striking a flat scintillator surface to insure that the particles will enter the surface near normal incidence, and so will tend to penetrate deeply into the crystal before scattering. The "hollow-crystal" detector (see Fig. 34b) proposed by Bell (8) reduces the backscattering contribution by collimating the electrons into a conical hole in the scintillator, from which the probability of escape is low for the scattered electrons. Hollow-crystal spectrometers have for several years been used to measure beta spectra, and they have consistently given improved performance over a flat scintillator, as regards both energy resolution and backscattering (83, 165). A set of plastic scintillators machined and polished for use in hollow-crystal detectors is available commercially.*

Because all organic scintillators are somewhat gamma-sensitive, it is necessary to correct any beta spectrum data for the gamma-ray background, if the source is gamma radioactive. For the detectors sketched in Figures 34a and b, this correction is obtained by interposing a beta absorber between source and detector, and using the resultant gamma-induced spectrum for a "gamma background." Such a correction is only approximate, because the shape of the background spectrum obtained in this way is distorted by the contributions from bremsstrahlung and scattered photons produced in the absorber.

Another method for reducing the consequences of scattering is to surround the source with scintillator, so that no scattered electrons are permitted to escape. This may be achieved in the "split-crystal" detector of Ketelle (123), shown in Figure 34c; here, the source is located between two scintillators arranged so that electrons scattered by one crystal are detected by the other. The nearly 4π geometry makes it difficult to measure the gamma-ray background with an absorber, and leads to a high probability that gamma-induced counts may sum with pulses from coincident beta particles to yield a very confusing spectrum. Excellent spectra of "inner" beta groups have been measured with a split-crystal detector in coincidence with gamma rays (193) by use of beta-gamma coincidence techniques discussed in Part 5.G of this section.

At low beta-particle energies (below about 200 keV), all of the methods described so far become rather difficult to apply, because the response is somewhat sensitive to the treatment of the scintillator surfaces, and the source must be very thin to be free from scattering and absorption effects. These obstacles may be overcome by adding the radioactivity directly to an organic liquid scintillator, and thus making the source an integral part of the scintillator (Fig. 34d). This is the basis of liquid scintillation counting, a technique which has found widespread use in chemistry, particularly in tracer experiments using low-energy beta emitters such as

---

* Nuclear Enterprises, Ltd., 550 Berry Street, Winnipeg 21, Manitoba, Canada.

C^{14}, S^{35}, Ca^{45}, and H^3. In some experiments it may be difficult to find a chemical form of the radioactive material which will not also quench the fluorescence. Because the subject of liquid scintillation counting, including such special topics as the use of suspensions and gels, has been reviewed in a volume of a companion series (221), it will not be treated further here.

In addition to the general arrangements discussed above, there are a few other counting techniques which make use of the versatile plastic scintillators for special applications. One such technique for the assay of solutions is the use of scintillator beads proposed by Steinberg (213). The detector is similar to that of Figure 34d, except the container is filled with small beads of plastic scintillator,* instead of a liquid scintillator. The radioactive solution whose activity is to be determined is poured into the container; the liquid fills the interstices between the beads, and thus puts the liquid and solid phases in intimate contact. A suitable solution must be transparent to the light from the scintillator and must not attack the plastic beads; although these solution requirements somewhat restrict the use of the technique, the preparation of a sample can be extremely rapid, and the beads can be washed and used repeatedly.

Plastic scintillators may be conveniently fashioned into many other shapes. Plastic scintillator dishes for containing radioactive liquids may be mounted directly on a photomultiplier tube for counting. Capillary tubing made from plastic scintillator can be wound into a spiral and attached to a photomultiplier to make a very simple flow counter for beta-radioactive gases and liquids.

Electron and Beta Spectrometry. In addition to their use as counters, these organic scintillators are useful for determining electron and beta-ray energies. The consensus of the available experimental information indicates a linear pulse height–energy curve down to a low energy of $\sim$100 keV; below this energy the response is also nearly linear, but with a slightly different slope (17).

The response of an organic scintillator to monoenergetic electrons is mainly a Gaussian peak whose width varies inversely with the square root of the energy. This energy dependence is predicted from the statistical variation in the number of photoelectrons at the photocathode and the electron multiplication processes within the photomultiplier tube; hence the contribution to the peak width by the scintillator itself is small. For an anthracene hollow-crystal spectrometer a resolution (full width at half-maximum counting rate) of about 10% can be achieved at 624 keV,

---

* Suitable beads are: "B-Beads" manufactured by Pilot Chemical Co., 39 Pleasant Street, Watertown 72, Massachusetts, or NE 102 Spheres, obtainable from Nuclear Enterprises, Ltd., 550 Berry Street, Winnipeg 21, Manitoba, Canada.

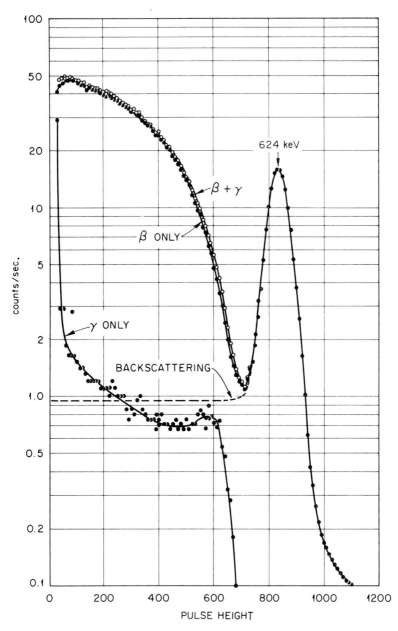

Fig. 35. Spectrum of a Cs¹³⁷ source, measured on a flat anthracene crystal. The internal-conversion electron line at 624 keV and the continuum from the 523-keV beta group are shown. When the beta rays and electrons are stopped in an absorber, the background spectrum from the 662-keV gamma ray is obtained. A coincidence between 624-k.e.v. electrons and their associated x rays excludes the beta and gamma spectra, and leaves only the electron line and its scintillator backscattering spectrum.

94

but if a plastic scintillator is used the resolution is only about 14%, because of the lower light output of the plastic.

Although the resolution of the electron scintillation spectrometer is poor compared to that of a magnetic spectrometer, the scintillation method has some appealing features. Used with a multichannel pulse-height analyzer (cf., Part 5.F, below) to display the distribution of pulse height ($\propto$ energy), it is possible to record the entire beta spectrum in a single counting interval; on the other hand, the magnetic spectrometer is a single-channel instrument, which can record only a single point on the spectrum at one time. The advantage of the scintillation spectrometer in studies of rapidly decaying sources is obvious. Further, the required scintillation detector is relatively inexpensive. Such simple spectrometers should find increased use in the analysis of mixtures of pure beta emitters, and in distinguishing between tracers which possess similar gamma-ray spectra.

Before a careful analysis of the beta spectrum shape can be made, the pulse-height distribution must be corrected for finite instrumental resolution. This is especially important for beta-ray end points below about 1 MeV. Corrections for finite resolution can be made using the method of Owen and Primakoff (168), and assuming that the scintillator response is a Gaussian whose width varies as $E^{-1/2}$. It was shown by Freedman et al. (76) that such a procedure corrected the spectrum near the maximum beta energy, but did not account for the excess of events at low energies. This excess counting rate arises from scintillator backscattering, which is never completely eliminated in a low-geometry arrangement (for example, the detectors of Figs. 34a and 34b). The typical response of a flat anthracene spectrometer to the electrons and beta rays from a Cs^{137} source is shown in Figure 35, which includes a spectrum due to the internal conversion peak alone. It is seen that the backscattering "tail" is essentially flat, and is about 6% of the peak height. Freedman et al. (76) developed an iterative method to correct the experimental data for both backscattering and resolution effects.

A comparison is made in Figure 36 between two Fermi plots (Section II.2.C) of the low-energy beta group of Cs^{137}. The upper curve shows the result obtained when the resolution distortion correction alone is applied, and the lower curve shows the improvement in the quality of the low-energy data when corrections are made for both resolution and backscattering.

The conventional correction procedures break down for beta groups below about 100 keV. This is because the resolution width becomes so large that most of the counts which appear to arise from events in the high-energy portion of the spectrum are actually due to low-energy elec-

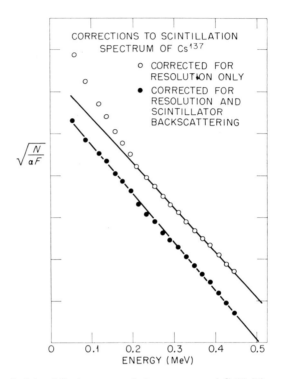

Fig. 36. Fermi plots of the low-energy beta-ray group of Cs[137]. The upper curve was corrected for the unique spectrum shape and the scintillation spectrometer resolution. The lower curve shows the improvement obtained when the correction for scintillator backscattering is included [Gardner (83)].

trons which fall within the detector resolution. Some idea of the resolution width at low energies can be gained by recalling that a good organic scintillation spectrometer with a resolution of 14% at 624 keV. (Ba[137m] conversion electrons) will exhibit a resolution of about 50% at 50 keV. These difficulties make it advisable to employ empirical corrections derived from data on low-energy beta emitters whose energies and spectral shapes are well known.

C. GAMMA-RAY COUNTING AND SPECTROMETRY

A most important contribution of the modern scintillation technique has been made in the field of gamma-ray detection. The much higher density of solid gamma-ray scintillators gives them a stopping power (i.e., detection efficiency) for photons far greater than gas-filled counters. It is now quite feasible to prepare scintillating crystals large enough to stop completely a sizeable fraction of incident gamma rays; thus it is possible not only to count gamma events, but also to measure energy spectra and gamma-ray intensities as well. The realization of these possibilities has put in the hands of the research chemist a versatile precision tool.

Scintillator Considerations. To be effective for gamma-ray detection, a scintillator should be of high density and high atomic number (see Section III.3); these requirements are best satisfied by the inorganic scintillators. Although there are many scintillating inorganic materials, only the activated alkali halides can be grown in single crystals of sufficient size, and yet possess the required transparency to their emitted light.

Sodium iodide, activated with 0.1% TlI, is the only alkali halide scintillator in routine use. It has the high density of the alkali halides, and has a moderately high effective atomic number. The light output in NaI(Tl) per million electron volts is the largest of any known scintillator, and is about twice that of anthracene. Large single crystals of NaI(Tl) are readily obtainable, and are highly transparent to their own fluorescent light, which is emitted in a band about 800 A. wide, centered at 4100 A. This wavelength is quite compatible with the response of standard photomultipliers having an S-11 response. (See the discussion of photomultipliers in reference 160.) The fluorescence decay time is 0.25 µsec., comparatively short for an inorganic crystal.

Because of its higher effective atomic number, thallium-activated cesium iodide has been investigated as a gamma-ray scintillator. At present, crystals of CsI(Tl) are far more expensive to manufacture than crystals of NaI(Tl). Further, although moderate pulse-height resolution can be obtained, the usable light output is only about 40–45% that of NaI(Tl). This lower apparent output may arise because the fluorescent light is emitted at longer wavelengths, namely, 4200–5700 A., and may not be measured efficiently by an S-11 photomultiplier tube. Improved pulse height could probably be achieved with a photomultiplier tube with better response in the red, such as the low-noise, multialkali-cathode tubes. The decay time of the fluorescent light from CsI(Tl) is 1.2 µsec., which is rather long for many applications.

Mounting Sodium Iodide Crystals. The method chosen for mounting a NaI(Tl) crystal on its photomultiplier tube involves a consideration of the deliquescence of the crystal, its optical properties, and the necessity for avoiding gamma-ray scattering. For some uses the two latter considerations may be relatively unimportant, but in all cases it is necessary to take great care that the crystal surfaces are not exposed to moisture. The usual procedure is to prepare a crystal for mounting in a dry atmosphere box; once mounted, the crystal enclosure should contain a dry atmosphere or else be evacuated.

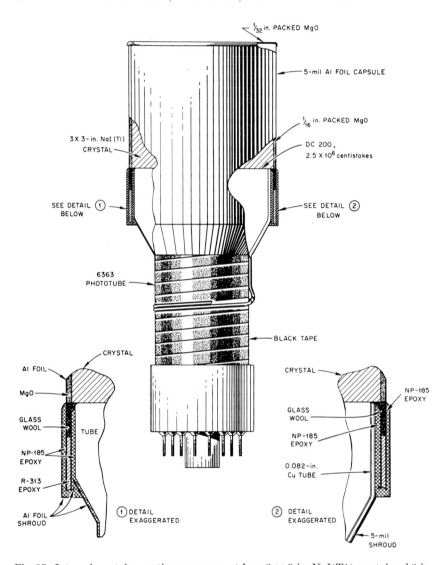

Fig. 37. Integral crystal mounting arrangement for a 3 × 3-in. NaI(Tl) crystal and 3-in. photomultiplier tube (V. A. McKay, Oak Ridge National Laboratory).

Whenever the largest possible light output is required, as in gamma-ray spectrometry, it becomes very important to gather the light and transmit it to the photomultiplier tube with the least possible attenuation. This is especially difficult when NaI(Tl) crystals of refractive index 1.77 must be optically coupled to glass faceplates with a refractive index of 1.5,

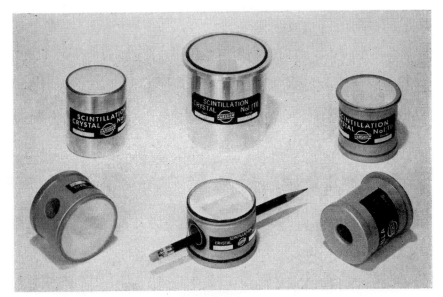

Fig. 38. Sealed NaI(Tl) crystal assemblies for a variety of applications. Transparent windows are provided for optical coupling to photomultiplier tubes (Harshaw Chemical Company).

because, if the surfaces are polished, much of the light tends to be critically reflected back into the crystal. The use of diffuse reflection at the crystal surfaces has been found to give higher and more uniform light output than specular reflection, since the probability is increased for light to be reflected onto the exit face of the crystal within the critical angle. The diffuse reflector surface is formed on the crystal by grinding all crystal surfaces, including the exit face. Any light escaping from the other crystal surfaces should also be returned by a diffuse reflector such as magnesium oxide or α-alumina.

If the NaI(Tl) detector is to be used as a spectrometer, it is important that any material surrounding the crystal be very thin. Otherwise, the gamma-ray spectrum will be distorted by Compton electrons and degraded gamma rays.

A crystal mount which used an enclosure fabricated from 5-mil aluminum, coated on the inside with a thin optical reflector of α-alumina, was devised by Bell and co-workers (8) for use where crystal and photomultiplier were of approximately the same diameter. Detailed procedures for fabricating the metal can and applying the reflector have been published (163). Figure 37 shows a crystal mount which is more easily mass-produced, and uses magnesium oxide powder as the diffuse optical reflector.

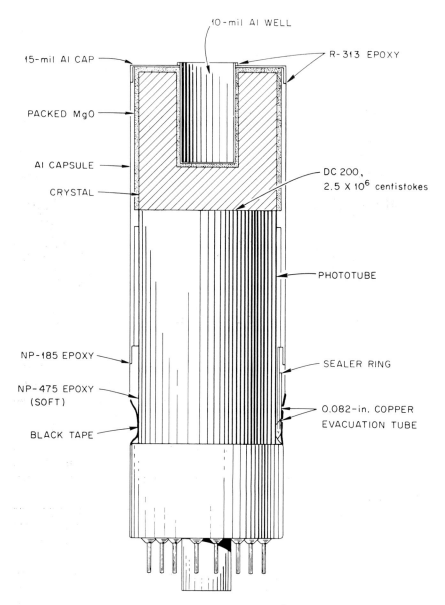

Fig. 39. An integral mounting arrangement for a 2 × 2-in. NaI(Tl) "well-type" crystal on a 2-in. photomultiplier tube (V. A. McKay, Oak Ridge National Laboratory).

Similar crystal-photomultiplier assemblies with good resolution are now available commercially.*

The light transmission from the crystal to the photomultiplier should be as efficient as possible; for this reason the crystal generally should be attached to the phototube by a single optical joint. In noncritical applications, such as simple counting, the loss of light from an additional optical seal and window may not be important. Here, an assembly is often used consisting of a crystal enclosed with its reflector in a thin can and optically coupled to a transparent window. Various crystal assemblies may then be attached to the same photomultiplier tube as required. Examples typical of such crystal mounts are shown in Figure 38.

Mounting NaI(Tl) crystals larger than about 3 in. in diameter calls for a more elaborate technique. Such large crystals are very heavy, and the mechanical problems involved in constructing a large detector make it necessary to relax somewhat the requirements of a thin container. The response of a large crystal is not as sensitive to scattering from the container walls as are the smaller crystals, for which the mass ratio of NaI(Tl) to cladding material is much less favorable.

Special Counting Problems. Whenever gamma-emitting nuclides are used in radiochemistry some variation of the versatile NaI(Tl) scintillation counter is nearly always used. It will be the purpose of this section to set down a few of the uses to which these counters have been put.

Perhaps the most generally useful configuration is the well counter (see Fig. 39). Various sizes are available; an inexpensive, yet efficient, detector is a NaI(Tl) crystal, at least 2 × 2 in., with a $^3/_4$-in. diameter well about $1^1/_4$ in. deep. Once the crystal has been mounted in a thin aluminum enclosure and a protective liner has been inserted to avoid the chance of permanent contamination of the crystal can, about $^1/_2$ in. of the original diameter will be left for insertion of samples. The well counter is the most sensitive gamma-ray detector available, and certainly one of the most convenient. To prepare a sample may only involve the transfer of a few milliliters of solution to a small test tube; because of the penetrating nature of gamma rays, self-absorption in such sources is small and further treatment of the sample to reduce the mass is usually not necessary. Commercial well-crystal counters are available which provide automatic sample changing and count recording for many samples.

In certain cases it may be desirable to assay large volumes of solution directly. A variation of the once-popular immersion counter is sketched in Figure 40; if a 3 × 3-in. crystal is surrounded by solution as shown, samples of several liters can be accommodated. A more compact assembly

* Harshaw Chemical Company, 1945 East 97th Street, Cleveland 6, Ohio.

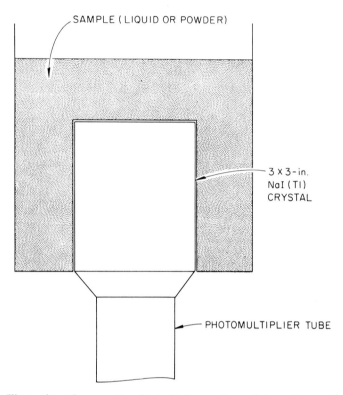

Fig. 40. Illustration of a way to obtain high counting efficiency for a scintillation counter used with large counting volumes.

uses a $^3/_4$-in. diameter NaI(Tl) crystal, 3 in. long. The manufacturer* states that the efficiency of this detector is one-fifth that of a typical well crystal with 5-ml. capacity, but has a sample volume 30 times greater.

The increasing need to make measurements of flow systems has led to several modifications of the scintillation counter for use with both liquids and gases. An excellent flow counter can be made from a length of plastic tubing either laid across the face of a NaI(Tl) detector or wrapped around it; or the tubing may be doubled into a U and inserted into a well crystal. Crystal packages are also available with a hole drilled through along a diameter, so that a tube passing through the crystal is surrounded by NaI-(Tl); an example is included in Figure 38.

Other special techniques which involve spectrometry rather than integral counting will be discussed in the following section.

Gamma-Ray Spectrometry. One of the most important applications of

* Atomic Accessories, Inc., 813 West Merrick Road, Valley Stream, New York.

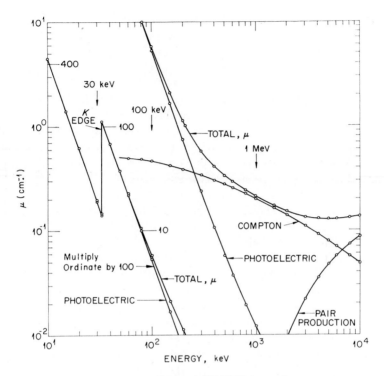

Fig. 41. Gamma-ray absorption coefficients in NaI(Tl) for various gamma-ray energies [Bell (8)].

the NaI(Tl) scintillation detector is in the field of gamma-ray spectrometry. Now that large, clear crystals of NaI(Tl) and photomultiplier tubes with uniform, high-efficiency photocathodes are available, it is possible to make a spectrometer which will not only measure energies of gamma rays to high precision, but also yield their intensities. Much of the popularity of the NaI(Tl) scintillation spectrometer in radiochemistry lies in its ability to differentiate between various gamma-ray components; hence, the presence of a particular nuclide in the spectrum of a mixture can be established by the characteristic energies observed, and the contribution of the nuclide can be determined quantitatively from the appropriate gamma-ray intensities.

Interaction of Gamma Rays in NaI(Tl). It should be recalled that gamma rays as such are not detected, but rather the secondary electrons produced by the interaction between the gamma rays and the crystal give rise to the fluorescent light. Thus it is appropriate to discuss first the three processes (photoelectric effect, Compton effect, and pair production) by which gamma rays interact insofar as they affect the scintillation spectrometer response; for a more detailed treatment see Section III.3.

Partial absorption coefficients in NaI for these processes are shown in Figure 41. Below about 100 keV, the photoelectric effect is by far the most probable; however, the photoelectric effect shows such a rapid decrease in absorption coefficient with increasing energy, that the Compton effect is left as the dominant process in the intermediate-energy region. Pair production, which sets in at 1.02 MeV and increases rapidly in probability thereafter, becomes the most important of the processes at very high energies. In all of these processes, it is predominantly the iodine of NaI which, because of its high Z, interacts with the gamma rays.

An attempt to demonstrate qualitatively the practical importance of the effects listed above is shown in Figure 42. The low-energy gamma ray γ_1 undergoes a photoelectric encounter within the first $1/8$ in. of material through which it passes. The photoelectron, which has a very short range, is stopped in the NaI(Tl) and gives up its energy to the crystal. The iodine atom which released the electron is left with a vacancy, most probably in its K shell; the act of filling this vacancy yields a K x ray. Usually the iodine x ray is captured by the crystal, for its energy is only about 28 keV; however, since low-energy gamma rays are always stopped near the crystal surface, there exists a small but significant chance that the x ray may escape the crystal surface entirely, and give a peak whose energy corresponds to the gamma energy minus the 28 keV of the x ray.

Above a few hundred thousand electron volts multiple processes play an important role, and so it becomes necessary to take into account the crystal size in addition to the various absorption coefficients. In Figure 42, γ_2 illustrates a Compton scatter by an intermediate-energy gamma ray. The Compton electron e_c is stopped and yields a light pulse proportional to the electron's kinetic energy; on the other hand, if the crystal is small the scattered photon γ_2' may not be stopped, and its energy will then be lost. The figure shows that in a larger crystal, further Compton processes may occur until the energy of the scattered photon is reduced to an energy so low that a photoelectric event finally transfers the remaining gamma energy to the crystal. It is important to bear in mind that the stepwise process just described occurs very rapidly compared to the speed of present-day electronic instruments; therefore, the interactions of γ_2 in the 3 × 3-in. crystal of Figure 42 would give rise to a single electrical pulse whose height would correspond to the total energy of γ_2.

Pair production introduces a very complicated response, as illustrated by the case of γ_3 in Figure 42. A high-energy gamma ray forms a positive and negative electron pair which carry off as kinetic energy the original gamma-ray energy, minus the 1.02 MeV (two electron rest masses) re-

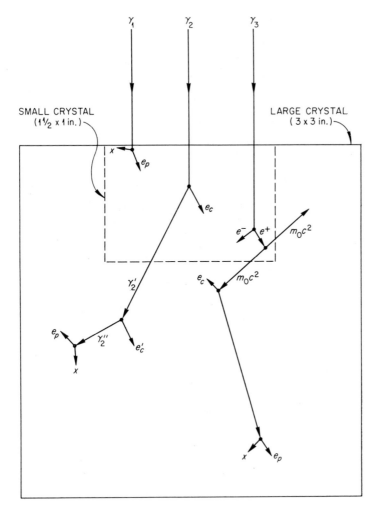

Fig. 42. Schematic representation of gamma-ray interactions within NaI(Tl) crystals of two sizes.

quired to create them. The two short-range electrons stop, and their kinetic energy is acquired by the crystal. The positron annihilates, forming two photons, each with an energy of 0.51 MeV (m_0c^2) and correlated at 180°. Once pair production occurs, the response depends on the probability that the annihilation photons will be captured. The example in Figure 42 shows that in a small crystal, the probability is greatest for the escape of both photons; in a larger crystal, it is more likely that at least one of the photons will be stopped. To summarize, then, the pair-production response leads to

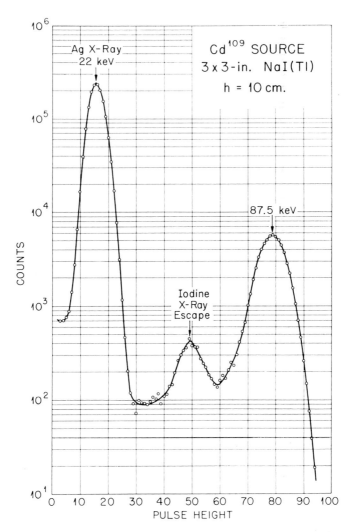

Fig. 43. Spectrum of 87.5-keV gamma rays and 22-keV x rays from a Cd[109] source, illustrating the phenomenon of x-ray escape following detection of 87.5-keV gamma rays.

three peaks in the pulse-height distribution: the full-energy peak, which corresponds to the capture of all the incident gamma-ray energy by the multiple processes; the "single-escape" peak, which signals the loss of one annihilation photon; the "double-escape" peak, which indicates the loss of both annihilation photons.

Typical Gamma-Ray Spectra. The effects just described are illustrated

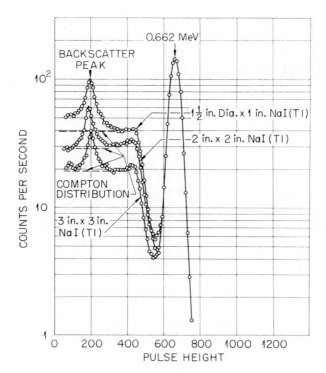

Fig. 44. Spectra obtained by measuring a Cs[137] source with NaI(Tl) spectrometers of three crystal sizes [Heath (104)].

by some representative gamma-ray spectra in Figures 43–45. More detailed explanations will be found in references 8, 51, 104, and 163. Because the light output from NaI(Tl) is very nearly linear with respect to the energy deposited, the distribution in the height of the pulses from various NaI(Tl) scintillation spectrometers will be treated as energy spectra. All of the gamma-ray spectra described below will have semilogarithmic intensity scales and linear pulse-height (or energy) scales. This has the decided advantage that the wide range of counting rates encountered in gamma spectrometry can be easily accommodated; further, spectral shapes can be compared by superimposing two spectra plotted on the same log paper with identical energy scales, even though the absolute heights of the peaks may be very different.

A typical spectrum from a low-energy gamma ray is shown in Figure 43. Although a large peak is present, arising from 22-keV x rays in the sample, let us direct our attention to the gamma-ray peak at 87.5 keV. Nearly all of the events in this peak are from the photoelectric effect near the crystal

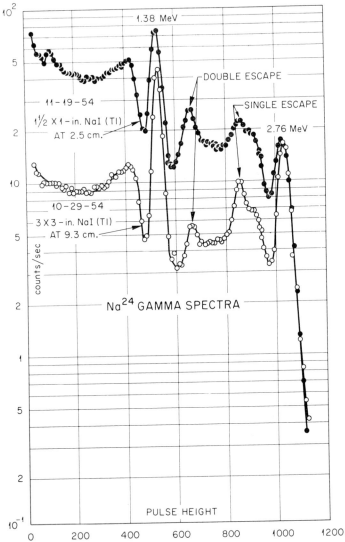

Fig. 45. Gamma-ray spectra of Na^{24}, using $1^1/_2 \times 1$-in. and 3×3-in. NaI(Tl) spectrometers.

surface (cf., γ_1 of Fig. 42); a peak about 28 keV lower is due to escape of the iodine K x rays. As the gamma-ray energy increases, the photons penetrate more deeply into the crystal before they undergo photoelectric absorption, and so the probability for x-ray escape diminishes; in addition, because the energy separation between the full-energy peak and the x-ray escape peak is a very small fraction of the gamma energy, the x-ray escape phenomenon is not observed above about 170 keV.

A comparison is sketched in Figure 44, which shows the spectra obtained at 0.662 MeV with NaI(Tl) crystals of different sizes. All of the spectra are normalized at the maximum of the full-energy peak. The smallest crystal yields a characteristic distribution below the main peak which results from an event in which a Compton-scattered photon is lost and the Compton electron is captured (cf., Fig. 42). It will be noted that as the crystal size increases, the probability for multiple processes also increases; this is manifested as an increase in the fraction of events falling within the main peak. Figure 44 shows that the ratio of the height of the full-energy peak to that of the Compton distribution is nearly twice as great for a 3 × 3-in. as for a $1^1/_2$ × 1-in. crystal. Of course, the more nearly the response approximates a single peak for a single gamma-ray energy, the more useful the spectrometer becomes.

The complexity of the spectrum when pair production is involved may be seen in the spectrum of Na^{24} shown in Figure 45. Two gamma rays are present in this source at 1.38 and 2.76 MeV. The full-energy peak and the two peaks stand out clearly in the high-energy portion of the spectrum. Note that in the smaller crystal there are relatively few multiple events leading to counts in the full-energy peak; in fact, the double-escape peak is the most intense of the three. This response may be contrasted with that of the 3 × 3-in. crystal, in which the contribution from multiple events has made the full-energy peak the most intense. Further, the probability of double escape is quite low. It may be of interest to note that the spectrum of the 1.38-MeV gamma ray shows no evidence of pair peaks; in practice, the effect of pair production is not detectable below about 1.5 MeV, even though the threshold falls at 1.02 MeV.

Environmental Effects. The gamma-ray spectra measured in a given situation will be complicated, in addition to the elementary interactions just described, by several important environmental effects. While space does not permit a complete treatment of such spurious responses here, a report by Heath (104) includes a valuable analysis of various experimental factors; some of Heath's findings as well as other related data will be found in reference 163.

In the discussion which follows it will be convenient to refer to Figure 46, which shows a typical arrangement for a 3 × 3-in. NaI(Tl) detector situated in a Pb shield.

One of the most persistent experimental difficulties is scattering, whose consequences may take various forms. Referring to Section III.3.B, it will be noted that, for large Compton scattering angles, the energy of the scattered photon is nearly independent of the incident gamma-ray energy, and

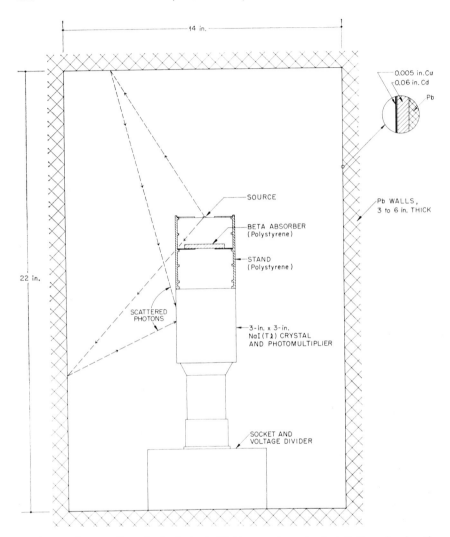

Fig. 46. Cross section of a typical scintillation spectrometer installation, showing the 3 × 3-in. NaI(Tl) detector assembly, the lead shielding with "graded" liner, and the use of a low-mass support for the source and beta absorber. The origin of scattered photons is illustrated.

attains an almost constant value around 200 keV. Thus, large-angle scattering from shield walls, source holder, or other matter in the vicinity of the source (cf., Fig. 46) will be manifested as a peak at about 200 keV. This peak is generally called the *backscatter peak*. It may be reduced by making the inside dimensions of the shield very large, thus decreasing the geometry between the detector and shield walls. Heath (104) demonstrated that a shield made from lead yielded a much smaller backscatter peak than one made from iron.

Another form of scattering arises from the beta-ray absorber usually placed between source and detector to stop beta particles or electrons in the gamma-ray source. Because of the geometry involved, the scattering is restricted to small angles, and so the scattered photons detected in the NaI-(Tl) crystal are only slightly reduced in energy. This has the effect on the gamma spectrum of filling in the "valley" between the Compton electron distribution and the full-energy peak.

Secondary radiation from the shield walls may cause serious complications. If bare lead walls are used in a spectrometer shield and a source of low-energy gamma rays is inserted, then fluorescent lead x rays are emitted from the walls and are detected by the NaI(Tl) crystal, causing a spurious 72-keV peak in the gamma spectrum. The mechanism for x-ray production is similar to that discussed above for x-ray escape from NaI(Tl) crystals. The best way to remedy this situation is to cover the lead surfaces with a sufficient thickness of a medium atomic number material, usually Cd, to attenuate the Pb x rays to a negligible level; the Cd is covered in turn by a thin veneer of Cu to absorb any fluorescent radiation from the Cd.

When very intense high-energy gamma rays are present in the source, it is common to observe a peak at 0.511 MeV in the gamma-ray spectrum. This peak is due to pair production in the Pb shield walls, with escape of annihilation radiation. Just as in the case of environmental scattering, the secondary radiation from the photoelectric effect and from pair production may be markedly reduced by increasing the separation between the shield walls and the source–detector combination.

Internal bremsstrahlung produced in the source and external bremsstrahlung emitted when beta rays are stopped in the absorber will be detected just as any other electromagnetic radiation. Therefore, when the number of gamma rays per beta disintegration is low, a prominent contribution from bremsstrahlung will be noted. Such an effect is shown as an upturn at low energies, with much the same shape as a decreasing exponential function added to the gamma-ray response (see Fig. 10).

Analysis of Gamma-Ray Spectra. The gamma-ray scintillation spectrometer has proved to be an important tool for the quantitative determination of gamma intensities. Since the true shape of the Compton electron distribution for a single gamma-ray energy is so easily obscured by the spurious effects which have just been described, the area of the full-energy peak is generally chosen as the basis for intensity measurements. The spectrum exhibited by a source which emits gamma rays of several energies will be a summation of the responses to the individual gamma rays. The

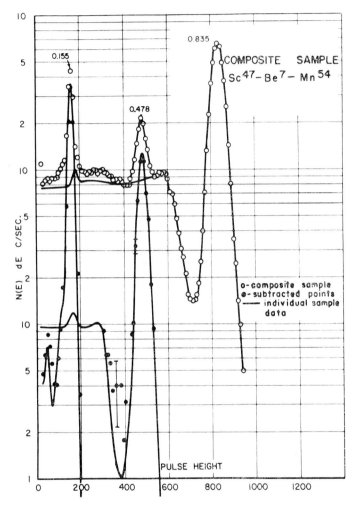

Fig. 47. Decomposition of a composite gamma-ray spectrum into its components by successive subtraction of standard spectral shapes [Heath (104)].

process by which accurate intensities may be obtained involves first breaking down the gross spectrum into its components (spectral decomposition), from which the area of the full-energy peaks may then be extracted.

The above discussion demonstrates that the pulse-height distribution of a NaI(Tl) spectrometer arising from the interaction of a single incident gamma-ray energy contains not just a full-energy peak, but in addition a complicated spectrum down to zero energy. In the course of performing a spectral decomposition, it is essential that the complete spectrum shape be used, and not just the full-energy peak. The detailed shape of the spectrum from a single gamma ray, or from a particular sample, is often called the *response function*.

The decomposition is relatively straightforward if the gamma-ray spectrum in question happens to be made up of gamma-ray components whose spectra can be determined individually. In such cases, the procedure to be followed simply involves normalizing the response function for the most energetic gamma ray to the experimental points at the full-energy peak; the response function is then drawn in and subtracted from the experimental data. The most energetic peak in the residue is fitted to the response function for that energy, and the subtraction process is repeated until all components have been "peeled off." An example of this process is shown in Figure 47.

It should be emphasized that the response functions must be determined under conditions identical with those under which the unknown was measured, so the response function used in the analysis will include the same spectral distortions, such as backscatter peaks, which affected the unknown. A frequently overlooked effect is the variation in gain with counting rate, which may occur in certain photomultiplier tubes and multichannel analyzers; for this reason it may be necessary to adjust the energy as well as intensity scales before attempting a point-by-point subtraction. Commercial devices exist which permit an adjustable fraction of a standard spectrum to be subtracted from a pulse-height distribution stored in a multichannel analyzer memory. When using a system such as this, it is particularly important that no serious gain shifts occur with changes in counting rate.

It may be impossible to measure directly the response functions for the component gamma rays of an unknown spectrum; in this case, it is necessary to synthesize the required function from a measurement of gamma-ray standards over the energy range of interest. The full-energy peak is nearly Gaussian, except on its low-energy side where the Compton spectrum contributes a slight distortion. Using standard spectra, the width parameter for the full-energy peak can be plotted as a function of energy, and values for the unknown can be evaluated. Other features of the spectrum can be constructed by interpolating on plots which correlate the coordinate (pulse height and counting rate relative to that for the full-energy peak) of various "key" points of the spectrum with the gamma-ray energy. Some of the key points which may be used are: the backscatter peak; the level, peak, and inflection of the Compton distribution; and the valley below the full-energy peak. If pair peaks are involved, their vital statistics must, of course, be included.

Once a particular full-energy peak has been resolved from the spectrum,

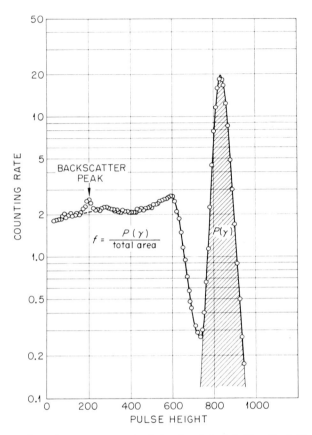

Fig. 48. Illustration of a measurement of the "peak-to-total" ratio f. Note that the backscatter peak is excluded from the total area.

the area under the peak $P(\gamma)$ may be obtained by summing the counting rates of the channels which contain the peak, or by means of the equation

$$P(\gamma) = a_\gamma\, h/[0.564\,(\Delta E)]$$ (38)

where a_γ is the half-width of the Gaussian peak at h/e; h is the peak height in the same units as $P(\gamma)$; and ΔE is the channel width. Both a_γ and ΔE must have the same units, and typically may be expressed in pulse-height divisions, channels, or keV.

Determination of Gamma-Ray Intensities. To obtain the intensity of gamma radiation emitted from the source, it is necessary to know the probability that a gamma ray from the source will strike the crystal, and the probability that an incident gamma ray will cause an event in the full-energy peak. The former probability is just the solid angle Ω for the par-

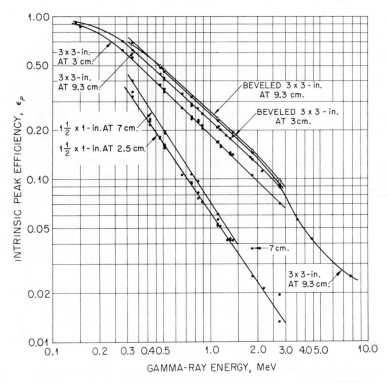

Fig. 49. Intrinsic peak efficiency ϵ_p for $1^1/_2 \times$ 1-in. and $3 \times$ 3-in. NaI(Tl) crystals [Lazar (136)].

ticular geometry, and the latter is often called the "intrinsic peak efficiency" $\epsilon_P(\gamma)$. Although it is very difficult to compute $\epsilon_P(\gamma)$ exactly, because of the multiple processes occurring within a large crystal, it is easy to compute the total intrinsic efficiency $\epsilon_T(\gamma)$, which is simply the probability that the gamma ray will produce a count once it strikes the crystal. The fraction of all counts in the spectrum which contribute to the full-energy peak is called the "peak-to-total" ratio, or "photofraction," and may be denoted by f (see Fig. 48). Then, $\epsilon_P(\gamma) = f \, \epsilon_T(\gamma)$. It is very important that, in the experimental determination of f, spectra be measured under conditions which reduce the effects of scattering as much as possible; otherwise, environmental scattering will add to the Compton electron spectrum and yield a high value for the area of the total spectrum.

Earlier it was mentioned that the full-energy peak was chosen for use in obtaining intensities because its area was free of spurious responses arising from the environment. Thus, once $\epsilon_P(\gamma)$ has been determined by the process just described, it may be applied to experiments having considerable differences in energy resolution and scattering conditions, just so the crystal dimensions and source-to-crystal distance remain the same.

Figure 49 presents values of $\epsilon_P(\gamma)$ for NaI(Tl) from the work of Lazar *et al.* (136), for $1^1/_2 \times$ 1-in. and 3 $\times$ 3-in. cylinders and a 3 $\times$ 3-in. cylinder with the top beveled at 45°, $^1/_2$ in. from the edge. Values of $\epsilon_T(\gamma)$ computed at Oak Ridge and the values of $\Omega \epsilon_T(\gamma)$ computed by Wolicki *et al.* (239) are compiled in a review by Mott and Sutton (160). Heath (104) and Vegors *et al.* (224) extended these calculations of $\Omega \epsilon_T(\gamma)$ to include point, line, and disk sources located on the axes of NaI(Tl) cylinders of different sizes; they also included measurements of *f* for use in the calculation of ϵ_P.

The number of gamma rays of a given energy $N(\gamma)$ emitted from the source may be obtained from

$$N(\gamma) = [P(\gamma)/\Omega\epsilon_P(\gamma)]e^{\mu d} \tag{39}$$

where $P(\gamma)$, $\epsilon_P(\gamma)$, and Ω have the same meaning as above; the factor $e^{\mu d}$ corrects for gamma absorption in any material between source and detector.

It often happens that the gamma ray of interest is coincident with another gamma ray (see discussion of decay schemes, Section II.3); in this instance the full-energy peak area will be decreased by coincident summing. This situation has been treated by Lazar and Klema (137), who derived an equation for obtaining the corrected emission rate.

Coincident summing of gamma rays leads to another important experimental implication. The gamma rays which are lost to their respective full-energy peaks appear in a "sum peak," whose apparent energy is the total energy of both gamma rays. Since the crossover transition for a simple gamma cascade will also be detected at this energy, such a peak must be corrected for the area of the sum peak through use of an equation derived by Lazar and Klema (137). Although the effect of angular correlations between the coincident gamma rays can often be neglected in summing calculations, Lazar and Klema have also shown how to apply, when required, the angular distribution function of the two gamma rays integrated over the face of the crystal (196).

D. DETECTION OF HEAVY CHARGED PARTICLES

As has been mentioned, the earliest application of the scintillation method was to the detection of alpha particles. In its modern form the scintillation counter has found extensive use in counting and spectrometry of other heavy charged particles as well.

Because of the short range of alpha particles, the scintillator may be made very thin. This also insures that the response to more penetrating radiations such as electrons and gamma rays will be small. The usual scintillator for counting is ZnS, activated by Ag. Although the light output is high, ZnS(Ag) is only available as a multicrystalline powder whose light transmission is poor; therefore, it is not used for measuring energy spectra.

The scintillator is usually deposited (35,194) by allowing ZnS(Ag) particles, $\sim$ 20 μ in size, to settle from a water or alcohol suspension onto a glass or plastic disk which will serve as a light guide. Typical scintillators made by this technique have a surface density of 5–25 mg./cm.². When the deposit is dry, it is usually sprayed with clear plastic or covered with a thin plastic film. Aluminizing the covering film improves the light collection efficiency and may be used to protect the phototube from ambient light. The total thickness of material covering the scintillator proper should be < 1 mg./cm.². Scintillator assemblies very similar to the above may be obtained from several manufacturers. The scintillator assembly is mounted by using silicon oil or grease as an optical coupling between the photomultiplier faceplate and the uncoated side of the glass or plastic light guide.

When it is desirable to use a scintillation device for determination of charged particle energies, some inorganic scintillator other than ZnS(Ag) must be used. Thin clear disks of NaI(Tl) or CsI(Tl) are often employed. The resolution of these devices cannot compare with the resolution obtained with a gas ionization or semiconductor detector, and so are not often used except in special situations. Further information on this subject may be found in recent reviews (161, 163).

2. Ionization Chambers*

A. IONIZATION IN GASES

Most of the experimental information about the stopping of charged particles in matter has been obtained from a study of the ionization produced. A very useful class of counters makes use of the ionization produced in a gas by collecting either the electron which is formed, or the *ion pair*, i.e., the electron and positive ion.

It will be recalled (Section III.1.B) that the specific ionization $d\vartheta/dx$, in ion pairs per centimeter of path, increases slowly to a maximum value a few millimeters from the end of the range, and then drops sharply. Specific ionization is related to the stopping power $-dE/dx$ by

$$d\vartheta/dx = - (1/w) \, dE/dx \qquad (40)$$

where w is the average energy to produce one ion pair (total ionization). The total ionization is of considerable practical importance, because the appropriate value of w can be used to predict whether a particular energy loss will render detection possible.

* See references 66, 80, 183, 198, 234, Franzen and Cochran in reference 210.

The value of w varies for different materials, but is remarkably constant for gases. For air, w is 34.2 eV, and for argon, a common gas for ionization detectors, w is 26.3 eV. Fulbright (80) recently has summarized the preferred values of w for gases of most interest in ionization devices.

The energy loss per ion pair is very nearly independent of particle energy and particle type. This immediately suggests that the integrated ionization $\mathscr{I}$ produced when an energy E is transferred, is given by $\mathscr{I} = E/w$. Although in most cases this proportionality can be assumed, there is some evidence that a nonlinear relationship between $\mathscr{I}$ and E exists for alpha particles less than about 0.1 MeV (80).

Once free electrons and positive ions are formed, their behavior depends upon the nature of the gas and the electric field present. An electron makes many collisions with gas molecules, and although its direction of motion is randomized by such collisions, there is a net drift in an electric field along a direction parallel to the field lines. The drift velocity depends on the type of gas, its pressure, and the electric field strength.

Positive and negative ions move much more slowly through gases than do electrons. Further, ionic mobilities are relatively insensitive to changes in the applied electric field strength and the gas pressure. Therefore, in the interest of fast response, pulse ionization chambers are almost invariably arranged for electron collection.

Electrons may form negative ions by attaching themselves to neutral atoms or molecules—this effect is especially harmful in pulse ionization chambers using fast electron collection. Of the common gases, the halogens, oxygen, and water vapor are the most serious offenders. The rare gases, hydrogen, nitrogen, carbon dioxide, and methane have attachment coefficients 10^3 times smaller than the halogens, and are considered acceptable filling gases for ionization detectors.

B. CURRENT CHAMBERS

The essential parts of a gas ionization chamber are two electrodes insulated from each other, defining a gas-filled space between them. A parallel-plate ionization chamber operated as a current chamber is sketched in Figure 50. The figure shows idealized current–voltage curves for a low- and a high-intensity source. At low applied voltage, there is a loss of charge through recombination of electrons and positive ions. As the potential is increased, the current flowing through resistance R from the collection of charge rises until it reaches a limiting value, the *saturation current*. At very high potential the current begins to rise again, due to the onset of gas multiplication (see Section VI.4).

The number of ion pairs formed per second, n, may be calculated from $\mathbf{R}$,

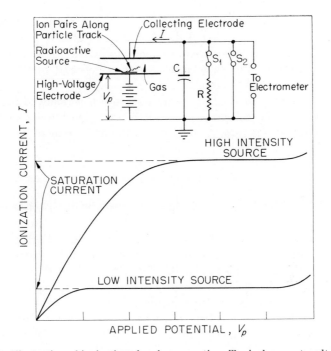

Fig. 50. Illustration of ionization chamber operation. Typical current–voltage curves are shown for different source intensities. The insert shows how a parallel-plate chamber is arranged for current measurement by the "IR-drop" method; for measurements by the "rate-of-drift" technique, both switches S_1 and S_2 must be opened (see text).

the rate at which particles are absorbed in the chamber, the average energy per particle $\bar{E}$, and w:

$$n = \mathbf{R}\,\bar{E}/w \tag{41}$$

The steady-state saturation current I is obtained by multiplying by the electronic charge e (1.60×10^{-19} coulomb): $I = en$.

Thus, if sources having identical energy spectra (i.e., the same $\bar{E}$) are compared, the saturation current is proportional to the source strength $\mathbf{R}$. This is the basis of the many ionization chamber instruments used for monitoring and assay purposes.

As shown in Figure 50, the current is always measured in terms of a voltage, using an electrometer. For this reason, the method just described is called the "IR-drop" method, because the voltage across R is given by the product IR.

The currents of interest lie in a range of about 10^{-8}–10^{-14} amp. The IR-drop method requires very high resistances for high sensitivity; however, in most cases it is not advisable to use resistors larger than 10^{12} ohms, if special techniques are to be avoided. When the rate $\mathbf{R}$ is very low, the statistical variations in the measured voltage require careful analysis if high accuracy is required. For these reasons the *rate-of-drift* method is used for small currents ($< 10^{-12}$ amp.).

In the rate-of-drift method, the load resistance R is removed by opening S_1 (see Fig. 50). The collecting electrode is grounded by closing S_2; thus the voltage across C is zero. At the start of the measurement S_2 is opened, and the voltage after a time t is given by

$$V = (1/C)\int_0^t I \, dt = It/C \tag{42}$$

The value used for C must include the combined capacitance of the chamber, leads, and electrometer input, and typically lies in the range of 10–30 picofarads; therefore, the sensitivity is very high. Further, because the rate of drift makes available to the electrometer all the charge produced in the time t, this method is fundamentally more sensitive than the IR-drop method, in which charge is continuously consumed by the load.

The theory and design of electrometers and the properties of insulators suitable for ionization chambers have been reviewed by Fairstein (66). Helpful suggestions on these techniques as applied to the determination of radioactive gases are given by Tolbert and Siri (221).

C. PULSE-TYPE CHAMBERS

When the rate of arrival of ionizing pulses is too low for convenient d.c. measurements, or when it is necessary to determine the energy distribution of particles stopped in the gas, the ionization chamber is operated as a pulse instrument. Here, the details of the collection process and the transient response of the auxiliary equipment are both very important, since the complicated signal from the chamber is always observed distorted by the measuring system.

Consider a parallel-plate ionization chamber in which a single ion pair has been formed (cf., Fig. 50). If the product RC is very large, the voltage across resistor R is $V(t) = q(t)/C$, where $q(t)$ is the *net* charge collected. It is important to note that the ion pair influences the net charge not only by being collected, but also by electrostatic induction. At the time of formation, the ion and electron are both at a distance x_0 from the collecting electrode, and because they induce equal charges of opposite sign, $V(0) = 0$. The electron moves rapidly to the collecting electrode, causing a linear increase in $q(t)$. During this interval the effect of the positive ion is negligible, as its transit time is about 10^3 times that of the electron. The important fact to note is that the expected final potential of $-e/C$ is not attained

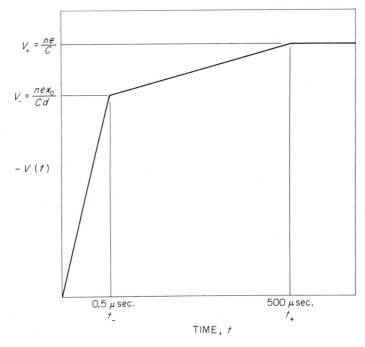

Fig. 51. Idealized voltage pulse in a parallel-plate ionization chamber with plate spacing d, after production of n ion pairs a distance x_0 from the collecting electrode. The electrons are collected at t^- and the positive ions at t^+. Note that the time scale is distorted to show the initial rise.

when the electron is collected, but only when the positive ion ceases to induce a charge, i.e., when the ion strikes the high-voltage electrode.

The collector potential for the process just described is sketched in Figure 51. The pulse profile shown makes the simplifying assumption that n ion pairs were formed at a point x_0: actually, the ionization is produced along a track, and the qualitative pulse shape in the figure will be distorted by the spacial distribution of ion pairs. Electron diffusion will tend to obscure the sharp changes in slope. From the discussion of ionization in gases it will be apparent that the presence of an electronegative gas such as oxygen will seriously distort the pulse.

As seen in Figure 51 the potential due to electron collection depends on the location of the ion pair at $t = 0$. This is not especially important if mere counting is required; the pulse must only be large enough to be recorded. However, some of the important applications for ionization chambers require a pulse whose height is proportional to the number of ion pairs. At first glance it may seem that one should amplify the pulse cor-

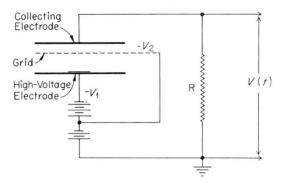

Fig. 52. Schematic diagram of a gridded ionization chamber. The source is mounted on the high-voltage electrode. The positive ions, which are all formed near the source, cannot induce a charge on the collecting electrode because of the electrostatic shielding effect of the wire-mesh grid.

responding to the total ionization, i.e., V_+ of Figure 51. Although this approach has been used very successfully, the amplifier required for broad, slow-rising pulses is prone to be rather noisy, and is very sensitive to microphonics and power supply hum. The tolerable rates are only a few per second, because of the danger that the pulses can "pile up." The slow rise time makes timing very uncertain, so that coincidence techniques are not very applicable (see discussion of electronic equipment in Part 5).

To avoid some of the difficulties encountered when total ionization pulses are collected, only the portion of the pulse due to electron collection is employed. Figure 51 shows that the electrons are collected in a much shorter time; it now remains to avoid the variation in pulse height with position of the ionized track. Two methods are used: either the collecting electrode is made very small, or it can be shielded by a grid.

The addition of a grid to a parallel-plate chamber is the most desirable technique for removing the effect of positive-ion induction (80,212,234) Such an arrangement is shown in Figure 52. The sample is placed on the high-voltage electrode; the gas pressure and geometry are so arranged that all of the ionization is produced in the region between the grid and the high-voltage electrode. The grid shields the collecting electrode from the influence of the positive charges, but the electrons are accelerated toward the collector. The charge at the collector is equal to the total ionization induced by the primary particle.

D. DESIGN CONSIDERATIONS

Because complete saturation can be attained with rather modest electrical fields, it is possible to design an ionization chamber to suit almost any

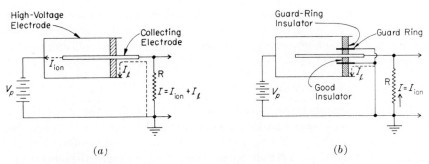

Fig. 53. Importance of guard rings in a cylindrical ionization chamber. (*a*) Without a guard ring, the measured current through load resistance R is the sum of the ionization current and the leakage current. (*b*) A grounded guard electrode assures that the high-voltage leakage current will not pass through the load resistor, so the current through R will be due only to ionization.

experimental arrangement. For current chambers the parallel-plate geometry is preferred, because it is the easiest design to analyze mathematically. Coaxial cylinder chambers are very easy to construct, and most of the ionization chambers in radiation survey instruments are of this type. Pulse-type chambers present a less critical design problem, because regions of weak field are of less concern than for current chambers.

In current chambers the placement and construction of the insulators are matters of the greatest importance, since the current flowing through the insulator should be negligibly small compared to the current flowing through the conductor it supports. Even materials of high resistivity may develop serious leakage currents if the surfaces are permitted to acquire a charge from mechanical stresses; from rubbing one surface against the other; or from the electric field, which can induce an image charge or cause ions from the active volume to be collected on the insulating surfaces (66).

On the other hand, ordinary surface leakage is not very important in fast pulse chambers at voltages of 1 or 2 kV. Small leakage currents can be tolerated, since the electronic system sees only fast transient signals; naturally, any corona discharge or other source of erratically changing leakage will cause bursts or spurious counts to be recorded.

Current chambers should always use guard rings. As shown in Figure 53, the guard ring serves two purposes: (*a*) When the guard ring is grounded, any high-voltage leakage is passed to ground instead of to the collector. Since only a small potential difference appears across the collecting electrode insulator, the collector leakage current is greatly reduced; (*b*) the active volume of the chamber is defined by the guard ring.

Guard rings are not always required in pulse chambers, and in some cases may lead to spurious counts. For example, the sensitive volume of a current chamber may be defined by a guard ring; but if the same chamber is operated in the pulse mode, ionization produced in the volume between the guard ring and high-voltage electrode can induce on the collector a pulse of detectable amplitude.

E. COUNTING AND ASSAY APPLICATIONS

Ionization chambers are widely used for measuring the strengths of sources of heavy charged particles. Very simple detectors can be made for routine alpha counting, if the energy distribution is not required.usually a spherical collecting electrode concentric with a cylindrical high-voltage electrode will suffice. To avoid random summing of low-amplitude pulses when a high beta- or gamma-ray activity is present in the alpha-particle source, a short clipping time is needed. A useful shortening of the detector rise time can be obtained by increasing electron drift velocity; in argon, a common filling gas, the rise time is improved by the addition of 5% CO_2.

The energy released in fission is nearly 40 times that for a 5-MeV alpha particle, and so fissions may be counted to the exclusion of other events. Parallel-plate pulse chambers are widely used for measuring fission cross sections and for intercomparison of fissile sources. If the number of alpha particles per fission event is very high, then the "pileup" of alpha pulses will cause a troublesome background; in such cases it would be advisable to use a detector with a more rapid response, such as, for example, a gas scintillation counter (164) or a semiconductor radiation detector (Part 3, below).

Ionization chambers also may be used for neutron detection. Fission chambers containing U^{235} are widely used as neutron-sensitive devices in reactor control and personnel protection. In some applications, chambers are filled with BF_3 gas, or lined with boron or lithium; the ionization is produced by the alpha particles and recoil nuclei from the (n,α) reaction on B^{10} or Li^6.

Low-energy beta emitters may be introduced as gases into a calibrated chamber for quantitative assay (Section VII.5). Ionization chambers may be used for relative assay of either gas or solid samples, even if the particles are not completely stopped in the gas (189). In this application the chamber must be calibrated for the particular beta activity and type of source mounting.

Current ionization chambers are particularly well suited to assay of gamma-ray emitters. A chamber designed with the proper regard for insulator considerations and mechanical rigidity should retain its calibration to a fraction of a per cent for years. Vibrating-reed electrometers are capable of measuring the saturation current with high precision ($\sim 0.05\%$). If standard gamma sources of known disintegration rate are used for ef-

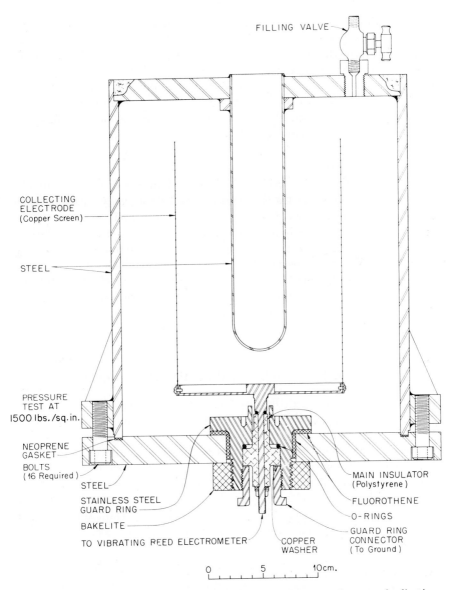

FILLING VALVE

COLLECTING
ELECTRODE
(Copper Screen)

STEEL

PRESSURE
TEST AT
1500 lbs./sq.in.

NEOPRENE
GASKET
BOLTS
(16 Required)
STEEL
STAINLESS STEEL
GUARD RING
BAKELITE
TO VIBRATING REED ELECTROMETER

MAIN INSULATOR
(Polystyrene)
FLUOROTHENE
O-RINGS
GUARD RING
CONNECTOR
(To Ground)
COPPER
WASHER

0   5   10cm.

Fig. 54. Design for a high-precision ionization chamber for secondary standardization of gamma-ray emitters. The chamber is filled with dry argon to a pressure of 40 atm. Samples are introduced via the re-entrant tube located inside the cylindrical collecting electrode [Stephenson (215)].

ficiency calibration, the chamber may be used as a precision secondary standard. Figure 54 shows the details of such a gamma-ray assay chamber, which is filled with 40 atmospheres of dry argon for high gamma-ray efficiency (215). Sources may be loaded either as solids or liquids in small bottles, which makes the arrangement free of complicated sample-preparation techniques. Because of the high sensitivity of the chamber, it is necessary to enclose it in a 4-in. thick lead housing as a means of reducing environmental background effects.

F. ENERGY SPECTRA

In several laboratories, gridded ionization chambers are used routinely for analyzing energy spectra of charged particles, especially alpha particles from radioactive samples. This method has been especially important in research on the transuranium elements. Good energy resolution (better than 1%) can be attained with large-area sources; background effects are very low; and the high geometry (nearly 50%) yields a high efficiency. The present "state of the art" has been reviewed by Hanna (98). Since the advent of the simple, high-resolution semiconductor detectors, many of the favorable arguments for grid chambers have been vitiated; however, the ionization chamber is still useful where both large sources and high geometrical efficiency are required.

3. Semiconductor Radiation Detectors

Basic understanding of the physics of semiconductors has evolved, for the most part, during the years following the invention of the transistor in 1948. The technology of semiconductor devices has proceeded hand in hand with the advances in basic science, and this combined effort of theorists and technologists has made a significant contribution to the detection and measurement of nuclear radiation. In this section we will discuss the use of p-n junctions and surface barriers as charged-particle detectors, an application which promises to become the most important innovation in radiation detectors since the development of the modern scintillation counter.

A. PRINCIPLES AND DESCRIPTION*

The semiconductor radiation detector behaves quite analogously to the gas ionization chamber, except that the charge is carried by electrons and electron vacancies (holes), instead of electrons and positive ions. Because

* For an introduction to the theory of semiconductor radiation detectors, see Brown, (31), and for an introduction to semiconductor devices in general, see Jonscher (116), Shive (205), and Henisch (107).

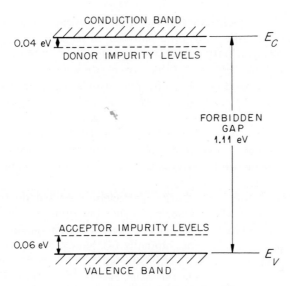

Fig. 55. Electronic band scheme for silicon.

of this similarity the device is often termed a solid-state ionization chamber. The use of a solid as a detector is very attractive, because the sensitive layer can be very thin and yet possess a high stopping power. Another advantage results from the low energy to produce one hole–electron pair (3.5 eV in Si): nearly eight times as much charge is produced for a given energy loss in silicon as in argon gas, which leads to smaller statistical fluctuations in the number of pairs and improved energy resolution over gas-filled counters. The intrinsically high speed of the device is due to the high mobility of the carriers in the electric field, coupled with the short distance between electrodes.

Introduction to Semiconductor Theory. Except at very low temperatures, a highly purified semiconductor exhibits *intrinsic conductivity,* as distinct from *impurity conductivity* of specimens which contain foreign atoms at some of the lattice sites. The electronic band scheme which explains this behavior can be discussed with reference to Figure 55. At absolute zero the conduction band is vacant, while the valence band is filled. As the temperature is raised, electrons in the valence band are transferred by thermal activation across the energy gap and into the conduction band. Both the vacancies (i.e., holes) in the valence band and the electrons in the conduction band contribute to the electrical conductivity, and are called *carriers.*

Apart from the intrinsic method of carrier excitation, electrons and holes may be introduced extrinsically from impurities or imperfections. Consider in particular the effect of impurities on silicon and germanium, which crystallize in the diamond structure with the chemical valence 4. If a penta-valent atom such as P, As, or Sb is substituted for a Si atom, there will be one valence electron left over. Such a pentavalent impurity is called a *donor*, because the energy level of the extra electron lies almost at the energy of the conduction band (see Fig. 55); and at most temperatures there is a high probability that the electron will be raised into the conduction band. Since the conductivity in this case is by negative charges, the material is said to be *n*-type. A trivalent atom such as B, Al, Ga, or In is called an *acceptor* because it can take on an electron from the valence band, leaving a hole; the resulting conductivity is due to the motion of the positive holes, and the material is said to be *p*-type.

The process of stopping a charged particle in a semiconductor results in lifting electrons from the valence and other low-lying, occupied bands to higher, unoccupied bands. Thus, electrons appear in nominally unoccupied bands and holes are created in nominally full bands. Interactions between electrons and holes cause the electrons to fall to the lowest available levels in the conduction band, while the holes rise to the highest levels of the valence band. The many states of this process, which are complete in about 10^{-12} sec., result in an over-all expenditure of 3.5 eV to produce one hole-electron pair in Si. It may be noted that this is about three times the 1.1-eV energy in Si, which is the minimum energy to produce a hole–electron pair. The additional energy is believed to be lost through strong coupling be-tween electrons and lattice vibrations of the solid.

The reader quite reasonably might ask why detectors are not made from materials with a smaller forbidden gap, and hence a smaller energy required to produce a hole–electron pair. In general, a material with a small forbidden gap can only be used at low temperatures; otherwise, thermal excitation of carriers will obviate its usefulness. Very good low-temperature detectors of Ge($w = 2.9$) have been made (228).

Production of High Fields in a Semiconductor. It is easy in principle to arrange the solid-state equivalent of a uniform field, parallel-plate ioniza-tion chamber; however, due to the small electrode spacing and the neces-sity for a high electric field to collect all of the charge, the resistivity of the material must be very high. Material of even the highest resistivity passes such a large current that the power dissipation at several thousand volts per centimeter would reach alarming proportions. More important are the random fluctuations in the current, which would be very large in proportion to the minute signal arising from the collection of hole–electron pairs at the electrodes. Thus, it is necessary to find some other way of sustaining a high electric field inside a solid without the use of high applied voltages, and without requiring high-resistivity material.

p-n Junctions. One way in which the necessary field may be obtained

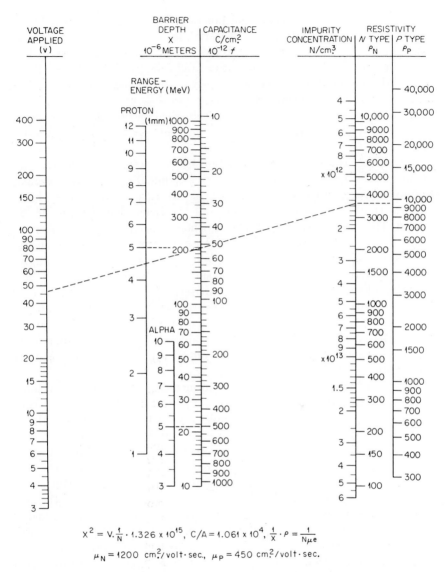

$$x^2 = V \cdot \frac{1}{N} \cdot 1.326 \times 10^{15}, \quad C/A = 1.061 \times 10^4, \quad \frac{1}{x} \cdot \rho = \frac{1}{N\mu e}$$

$$\mu_N = 1200 \ cm^2/volt \cdot sec., \quad \mu_P = 450 \ cm^2/volt \cdot sec.$$

Fig. 56. Nomograph which relates the applied reverse bias voltage, barrier depth, dynamic capacitance, and impurity concentration for a Schottky-type barrier in silicon. The impurity concentration may be found by using the resistivity in ohm-cm. of the base material used. Also included are ranges of charged particles in silicon corresponding to particular barrier depths [Blankenship and Borkowski (19)].

is by means of a reverse-biased, *p-n* junction. This device is usually fabricated from high-resistivity *p*-type material, into which a small amount of donor impurity, such as phosphorus, has been diffused to a depth of less than one micron. At room temperature, diffusion of electrons and holes will build up a negative charge on the *p*-type region and a positive charge on the *n*-type region. There now exists a *space-charge region*, or *depletion layer*, in which the acceptors are completely filled and the donors are completely empty. A potential barrier is now present because of the separation of charge.

If a voltage is applied to the junction by connecting the negative terminal to the *p*-type region and the positive terminal to the *n*-type region, the junction is said to be *reverse-biased*. As this reverse bias voltage is increased, the barrier height increases and the space-charge region is extended. The exhaustion-layer theory of Schottky (4) has been very successful in accounting for the properties of potential barriers and space-charge regions in semiconductors. The nomograph of Figure 56 is useful for applying the Schottky theory to practical silicon diodes. If the applied bias voltage and the resistivity of the base material (*p*-type silicon in the case just described) are known, the barrier depth x may be quickly determined. Since the depletion layer is the only region containing a high field for collection of charge, the experimenter must be able to estimate x in order to be certain that incident particles will be stopped within the sensitive part of the counter.

Note that the nomograph in Figure 56 includes values for the dynamic capacitance in picofarads per square centimeter. This capacitance arises because the space-charge region resembles two charge sheets of finite thickness, separated by a thin, high-resistivity layer, the barrier itself.

A modification of the *p-n* junction detector, which has produced sensitive regions deep enough even for beta particles of several million electron volts, makes use of the "ion-drift" technique investigated by Pell (176). A junction is formed on *p*-type silicon by diffusing lithium into the surface; the lithium finds its way into interstitial positions, and acts as a highly mobile donor. At elevated temperatures and with a reverse bias applied, the concentration of Li^+ ions will adjust to compensate precisely for the acceptor concentration. In effect, a deep intrinsic region is formed within the *p-n* junction.

Elliott (62) has fabricated and evaluated detectors made by ion drift. He was successful in producing detectors with $x = 0.338$ cm., which corresponds to the range of 96-MeV alpha particles, 24-MeV protons, or 1.7-MeV electrons. A Li-drifted diode having a depletion layer 0.20 cm. thick (or an electron range of 1.1 m.e.v.) gave an energy resolution of 2.5% at 624 keV electron energy, most of which was due to electronic noise.

The ion-drift technique therefore appears to be a very promising method for attaining thick depletion layers at room temperature.

Surface Barriers. A second general class of semiconductor device which can build up a high electric field for the collection of charge is the *surface barrier* detector, which is usually made from high-resistivity, n-type silicon. Although the detailed mechanism is not well understood, the nature and formation of the surface barrier is believed to arise from surface states, whose existence is well established for silicon and germanium (125). These surface states are able to trap electrons from the n-type crystal. The high density of electrons on the surface and the positive charge on the bulk combine to distort the energy levels E_v and E_c (cf., Fig. 55) near the surface, and a potential barrier results. An analysis shows that this situation closely resembles a p-n junction in which the bulk is n-type, and the surface is p-type.

With reverse bias applied, the depletion region widens very much as was observed for the p-n junction. In fact, the theoretical treatment used to obtain the nomograph in Figure 56 does not distinguish between barriers formed at p-n junctions or at surfaces.

Collection of Charge. Many of the general remarks on the operation of gas ionization chambers apply equally to the semiconductor type. It will be recalled that, in gas ionization chambers, the low mobility of heavy positive ions gives rise to several problems associated with the collection of charge; on the other hand, the semiconductor detector possesses the great advantage that both the hole and the electron are highly mobile current carriers. In silicon at room temperature the electron mobility μ_n = 1200 cm.^{2}/volt-sec. and the hole mobility is μ_p = 500 cm./volt-sec. This situation makes it possible to collect all the charge in a short time, regardless of the location of the event within the depletion layer, and so the output pulse height is largely independent of such geometrical effects, although the rising portion of the pulse may show some variation in shape.

The charge q collected for an average energy $\bar{E}$ dissipated in the sensitive region is

$$q = e(\bar{E}/w)\eta \tag{43}$$

where w is the energy to produce one hole–electron pair (3.5 eV for silicon), and η is the collection efficiency. In a good diode, it should be possible to increase the bias to the saturation value, i.e., to a bias for which $\eta = 1$.

The signal voltage appearing across the detector is readily obtained from the charge q, and the sum of the barrier capacitance C_b and the stray capacitance C_s:

$$V = q/(C_b + C_s) \tag{44}$$

Note that, for a strictly proportional relationship between V and q, both C_b and C_s must be constants.

B. FABRICATION TECHNIQUES

Semiconductor radiation detectors resemble conventional photovoltaic cells, and the usual semiconductor fabrication methods (16) are followed. In this section, emphasis will be given to silicon diodes, because they are suitable for room-temperature operation; however, excellent detectors for operation at liquid-nitrogen or liquid-helium temperatures have been made by using germanium as base material (228).

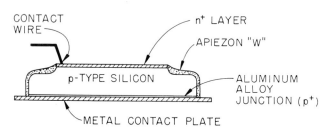

(a) JUNCTION

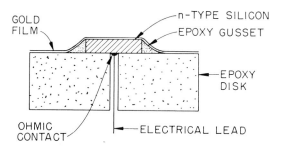

(b) SURFACE BARRIER

Fig. 57. Sketches showing semiconductor radiation detector construction (not to scale). (a) p-n junction detector. (b) Surface barrier detector.

Diffused Junctions. A typical diffused junction diode is shown in Figure 57a. The wafer of p-type silicon is approximately 5 × 5 mm., and about 1 mm. thick.

The heavily doped, so-called n^+ layer is prepared by diffusing phosphorus to a depth of about 0.1 micron; afterward, a deep etching is made, which removes not only the excess n^+ material, but also the p-type substrate to a considerable depth. This leaves the so-called "mesa" configuration shown in the sketch.

A metal contact to the high-resistivity p-type silicon must be carefully designed, otherwise an injecting contact may develop, with erratic results. If a pressure contact is to be used, an alloy junction is made by alloying an acceptor metal such as aluminum with the high-resistivity base. This forms a heavily doped, or p^+ layer, to which a pressure contact may be made with ease.

Because of the heavy doping of the n^+ layer, an Ohmic contact to it is readily made. A gold, or even a copper, wire is put in pressure contact with the n^+ layer. The contact is improved if a 0.01 μf. capacitor, charged to several hundred volts, is discharged through the diode in the forward bias direction. As shown in Figure 57a the junction edges should be protected by painting with Apiezon W dissolved in trichloroethylene. The general procedure just described resembles a technique by Donovan (61).

Surface Barriers. The surface barrier detector shown in Figure 57b also is made from a silicon wafer about $5 \times 5 \times 1$ mm. The Ohmic contact is made by soldering to a surface which has been nickel-plated. The top surface is carefully etched and the wafer is mounted on an epoxy disk. A smooth gusset of epoxy resin is flowed around the wafer, so that all edges are protected. A thin layer of gold ($\sim$ 100 μg./cm.^{2}) is then deposited by vacuum evaporation over the entire top face of the assembly, to form a conducting layer. Electrical connection to this layer is made by pressure contact to the top face of the epoxy disk. Lower leakage currents and higher inverse voltage breakdowns will be obtained if the finished detectors are baked for 48 hr. at 110°C. Because of their sensitivity to ambients, surface-barrier detectors should be stored in a vacuum desiccator before use.

The design just outlined follows the technique of Blankenship and Borkowski (19), with some modifications by Chetham-Strode et al. (45).

C. APPLICATION TO SPECTROMETRY

Electronics. A typical electronic system for use with a silicon surface-barrier detector is sketched in Figure 58. The bias supply must be well filtered. It is usually helpful to monitor the leakage current as the bias voltage is varied.

Because signals from the detector are of such low amplitude, the preamplifier should be very carefully designed for low input noise. It is also recommended that the preamplifier be of the "charge-sensitive" type (see Part 5.B of this Section), which produces an output pulse whose amplitude is proportional to charge and not voltage. A voltage-sensitive amplifier will reflect any variations in the input capacitance resulting from variations in the barrier properties (cf., eq. 44); such irregular changes in capacitance do occur, but are not serious if the amplifier is charge-sensitive.

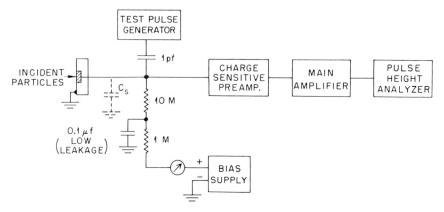

Fig. 58. Functional block diagram of equipment used with a surface barrier detector.

A test pulse generator with low-impedance output may be used for check-ing the operation of the system. When used as shown in Figure 58, the gen-erator may be calibrated in terms of energy and will, for a given generator amplitude setting, deliver the same amount of charge to the preamplifier, even though the input capacitance may vary greatly. Its output is a useful substitute for a detector pulse. The noise of the system with an equivalent capacitance substituted for the detector may be measured by injecting an amount of charge corresponding to some given energy, and from the width of the peak obtained the amplifier noise may be calculated. The equivalent noise from such a measurement typically is 3–10 keV full-width at half-maximum.

The clipping time of the main amplifier may be chosen for optimum signal-to-noise ratio, since the collection time is extremely rapid compared to gas ionization chambers. Recommended clipping times are 0.5–2 μsec. (19).

Experimental Arrangement. Semiconductor detectors have been applied to the study of many types of charged particles. Perhaps the most success-ful application of interest to chemists is in high-resolution alpha spectros-copy, although recent advances in technique indicate that these detectors may eventually find even more widespread use in electron and beta-ray energy studies.

Figure 59 shows the counting chamber designed by Chetham-Strode, Tarrant, and Silva (45) for precision alpha spectrometry with silicon sur-face-barrier detectors. The relatively large internal dimensions were chosen to remove scattering surfaces from the source and detector. The detector was recessed so that the sensitive part of the detector could not "see" the scattering surfaces. Since the surface-barrier detector is rather sensitive

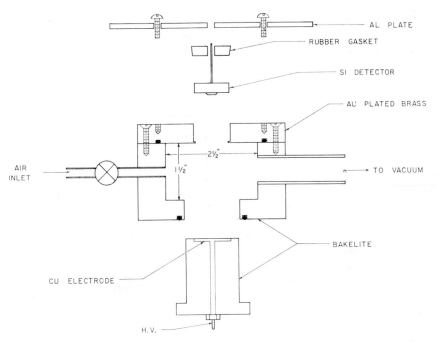

Fig. 59. Exploded view of a chamber for study of alpha-particle spectra with a surface barrier detector [Chetham-Strode *et al.* (45)].

to air ambients and the alpha-particle energy is degraded by air, provision was made for evacuating the chamber.

The technique to be followed was treated in detail by Chetham-Strode *et al.* (45), who discussed the problem of eliminating background counts in order to realize the inherently low background possible with silicon detectors. Materials of construction used in the counting chamber should have very small alpha contamination. In cases where the recoil daughter nuclei formed in alpha decay are radioactive and may contaminate the silicon detector, these authors suggest introducing a low gas pressure into the chamber to slow the recoils to an energy such that they can be returned to the source plate by application of an electric field.

An alpha spectrum of Cm^{244} obtained with a surface-barrier detector is shown in Figure 60. The full-width at half-maximum counting rate is only 16 keV and so the two main alpha groups, 43 keV apart, are well resolved. In addition to the groups shown, a third group, 142 keV below the intense peak (α_{142}) is known (230) to be present in an abundance of 0.017%. Since the resolution is adequate, it would be hoped that measurement of such low-abundance groups could be accomplished on sources with too low an intensity to measure by magnetic deflection. Such weak alpha groups may often be obscured by a non-Gaussian, low-energy tail on the peaks. The height of this tail at the expected position for the α_{142}

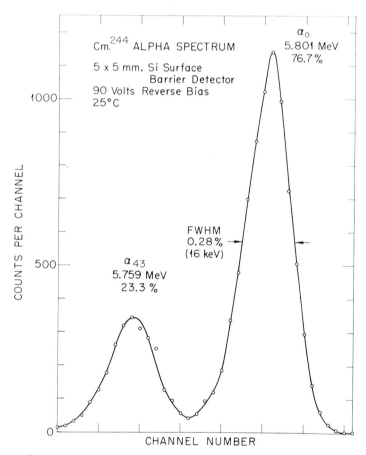

Fig. 60. Pulse-height distribution measured with a 5 × 5-mm. silicon surface-barrier detector at 25°C. and 90 v. reverse bias. The energies and abundances of the alpha groups to the ground and 43-keV states of the Pu^{240} daughter nucleus are literature values [A. Chetham-Strode, Oak Ridge National Laboratory].

peak of Cm^{244} is 0.15% the height of the α_0 peak. From information available to date, it appears that a substantial portion of this tail is associated with processes within the detector proper, and not with environmental effects such as source properties, scattering, or energy loss in the gold detector film.

4. Gas Multiplication Counters

A. INTRODUCTION

The operation of an ionization chamber depends upon the collection of the charge produced when an ionizing particle traverses the sensitive volume. Any enhancement of the electrical signal produced must be done in the electronic amplifier system, as the chamber possesses no internal amplification properties. On the other hand, proportional counters and Geiger counters make use of *gas multiplication*, which enables them to produce output pulses many times larger than would be obtained if only the primary ionization were collected.

The distinction between simple ionization chambers and gas multiplication counters may be seen by considering the number of ion pairs collected (or pulse height) as a function of applied voltage. For example,

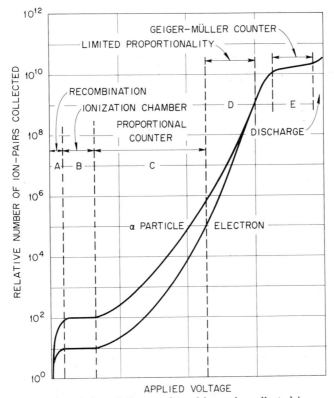

Fig. 61. Illustration of the relative number of ion pairs collected in a counter as a function of the applied voltage, showing the relationship between the ionization chamber, proportional counter, and Geiger-Müller counter regions of operation.

Figure 61 shows the behavior of a gas-filled counter with coaxial electrodes; the inner electrode is a fine wire, which serves as the anode. As was shown in Section VI.2, the number of ion pairs collected rises with applied voltage, until a saturation region (B of Fig. 61) is reached. When the voltage is advanced beyond region B, the electrons acquire sufficient energy near the anode to produce additional ionization of the gas by collision, and the pulse height rises. Throughout region C, each electron produced initially will produce an avalanche of m secondary electrons; m is called the *gas multiplication*. Region C is referred to as the proportional counter region, because the pulse size is proportional to the initial ionization; hence, the pulse height from the alpha particle of Figure 61 remains a factor of 10 higher than the electron pulse height. This suggests that alpha particles can be counted in the presence of electrons, which usually have a lower energy: a pulse-height discriminator (cf., Part 5, this section) may be set to reject the low-amplitude electron pulses and count only the alpha particles.

Eventually, a further increase in voltage creates such a density of secondary charges near the anode that the positive-ion space charge from one primary electron begins to interfere with the formation of an avalanche by a neighboring electron. This effect leads to the situation in D of Figure 61 where the different amounts of primary ionization produce slightly differing pulse heights, but the strict proportionality is lost.

Region E is the Geiger-Müller region, in which the detector produces a pulse of essentially constant height, regardless of the initial ionization. In this mode of operation the discharge is not localized, but rather a single electron initiates an avalanche which propagates throughout the anode's length. Although the Geiger-Müller counter, or Geiger counter as it is often called, cannot be used for spectrometry, its large-amplitude output pulse makes it useful for many applications where simple counting will suffice.

B. PROPORTIONAL COUNTERS*

Proportional counters are especially useful where pulse counting of beta radiation is required. Because of their shorter resolving time, proportional counters can be used at much higher counting rates than a Geiger counter, and they exhibit excellent long-term stability. When used as a spectrometer for low-energy beta rays and x rays, the proportional counter is capable of much better resolution than a scintillation spectrometer.

Conditions for Gas Multiplication. To achieve gas multiplication it is necessary to provide an electric field strength capable of accelerating the

* See references 48, 52, 53, 184, and 234.

primary electrons to an energy sufficient to produce additional ionization. In a typical geometry, the anode is a fine wire of radius a, coaxial with a cylindrical cathode of radius b. The electric field strength ε, at a radial distance r, and an applied voltage V, is

$$\varepsilon = V/[r \ln (b/a)] \tag{45}$$

It is apparent from equation 45 that the high field is confined to the region near the central wire; hence, most of the gas multiplication occurs within a few mean-free paths of the anode. Since the electrons move such a short distance before they are collected, the voltage pulse which appears on the anode arises from induction by the positive ions as they move away from

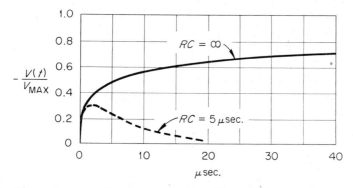

Fig. 62. Shape of a proportional counter pulse. The dotted curve shows the shape obtained with an input time constant $RC = 5$ μsec. [Staub (212)].

the central region. The formation of a voltage pulse in this way is not as slow as might be expected, because the positive ions move through most of the voltage drop while still in the high-field region near the central wire. The time to collect all of the ions depends on the geometry, applied voltage, the gas chosen, and its pressure (234); generally, collection times are a few hundred μsec.

The pulse shape (212) for a single ion, or a group of ions produced at the same place, is shown in Figure 62. The output voltage rises very rapidly at first, being nearly linear with time; later, the pulse shape becomes logarithmic. In the example of Figure 62, the pulse reaches half of its maximum amplitude in about 5 μsec.; the total collection time in this case would be 590 μsec. If the time constant is reduced to 5 μsec., the maximum pulse height drops to about one-third of the former value, but is much narrower. By "clipping" or "differentiating" the pulses in this way, the pulse width can be made small enough to permit high counting rates. Note that in this procedure all pulses are reduced by the same factor, since the final pulse height in a proportional counter does not depend on the location of the primary ionization. However, there will be some variation in the rising part of the voltage pulse if the primary electrons are distributed radially through the chamber, since the primary electrons will then require a varying amount of time to drift into the multiplication region. For this reason, it is customary to integrate the signal with a time constant equal to several times the signal rise time to reduce the effect of rise-time variations on output amplitude (87).

The gas multiplication factor for a proportional counter may vary over a wide range. Actual values for particular filling gases are obtained experimentally as a function of applied voltage, chamber geometry, and gas pressure. Usually, gas multiplications range from unity up to about 10^4, with values as high as 10^6 possible for events with low primary ionization; the onset of nonproportionality is observed to occur with particles of high primary ionization at lower multiplications than minimum ionizing particles (see Fig. 61).

Construction and Use. Many practical forms of proportional counters have been employed. The design chosen usually depends on the application—for spectroscopy, the requirements may be quite exacting, while for beta counting, the design is not so critical.

When the proportional counter is to be used for spectroscopy of low-energy electrons or x rays, the electric field should be uniform and the electrical noise generated by insulator leakage must be very small. The former requirement can best be met by using a cylindrical geometry, and then only if the central wire diameter is very uniform. It can be seen from equation 45 that small variations in the central wire diameter will cause large variations in the electric field strength. Any practical design will lead to some distortion of the electric field at the ends, the so-called "end effect." However, if the radiation to be analyzed can be collimated so that only the center portion of the sensitive volume is illuminated, then the end effect will not be very serious, provided that the counter tube is long with respect to its diameter. Such a design is shown in Figure 63; low-energy x rays are permitted to enter the counter through a beryllium window, midway along the wall.

Occasionally it may be inconvenient to make a long counter; a considerable latitude in dimensions is possible without field distortion if electrically insulated field tubes (52) are placed over the guard tubes. Their voltage is adjusted so that the lines of force are radial at the end of the sensitive volume.

Figure 63 also serves to illustrate how the requirement of low leakage noise is met. First, a guard electrode is used in the same way as for ionization chambers. Also, the anode is operated at ground potential, so there

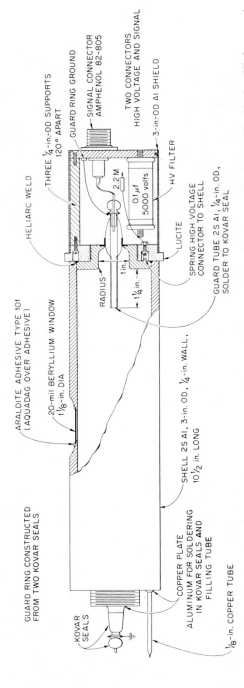

Fig. 63. Proportional counter for x-ray spectrometry, showing details of construction (C. J. Borkowski, Oak Ridge National Laboratory).

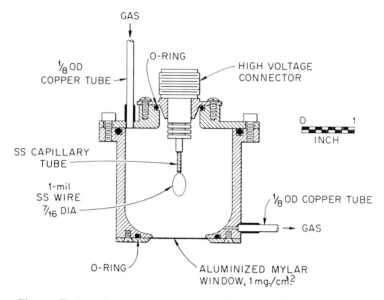

Fig. 64. End-window proportional counter for routine beta-ray counting.

is no need for a high-voltage blocking capacitor, which often can become a source of noise.

Because they are so much more convenient and reliable than Geiger counters, most routine beta assay work is performed with proportional counters. Often it is neither practical nor necessary to approximate a cylindrical geometry for an end-window counter; in this case, the design of Figure 64 is useful. A wire loop is the anode and may be placed inside a cylinder as shown, or inside a hemisphere (Fig. 76b). These counters are usually operated at 1 atm. pressure of filling gas, which flows continuously. If pure methane is used as the counter gas, a rather high voltage (typically 3500 V.) is needed; a mixture of 90% argon and 10% methane (P-10 gas) permits operation at about half the methane voltage.

In a flow counter the window may be eliminated entirely. This is especially helpful in the counting of alpha particles and low-energy electrons. The sample is introduced into the chamber by means of a slide.

The 4π counter has enjoyed increasingly widespread use in the standardization of radioactive sources (cf., Part 7.B). A useful version of this type of counter is shown in Figure 65. Two identical proportional counters view the source with almost an exact 4π geometry. The chambers are of the "pillbox" type with 1-mil stainless steel anode wires. When used for absolute beta counting, the anodes of the two halves are connected together and operated as a single counter. A slide is provided for rapid chang-

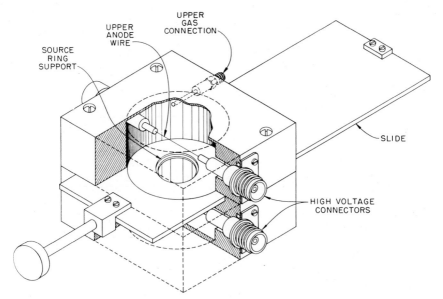

Fig. 65. Proportional counter for 4π beta counting (Oak Ridge National Laboratory Model Q-1632).

ing of samples. The carrier-free source is mounted on a thin plastic film, metallized to insure electrical conductivity; thus, the source film cannot acquire an electrostatic charge, but remains a part of the ground plane dividing the two counters.

Plateau Characteristics. For alpha and beta counting the required voltage sensitivity is about 1 mV. This is obtained, for example, if the amplifier voltage gain is 250, and the scaler or other recording equipment records all pulses above 0.25 V. As the voltage is increased, the counting rate rises until all particles yield a pulse large enough to register; increasing the high voltage still further produces an essentially constant counting rate, since all particles are now being recorded. This region of almost constant counting rate is called the *plateau*.

In Figure 66 is shown a counting rate–voltage curve obtained with a source containing both an alpha and a beta emitter. The alpha particles deposit more initial ionization than the beta particles, and so a smaller gas multiplication is needed to count them. The figure shows that the alpha-particle plateau is reached several hundred volts before the beta-particle plateau.

A well-designed proportional counter will have a plateau of negligible slope ($<0.2\%/100$ V) for several hundred volts, when counting beta particles having energies greater than about 200 keV. This performance

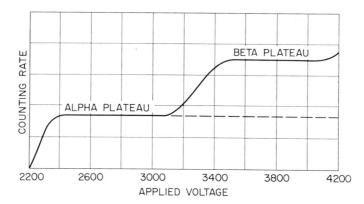

Fig. 66. A counting rate–voltage curve obtained with an end-window proportional counter and a source containing both an alpha and a beta emitter.

can only be obtained with an amplifier having low noise and good overload properties (see Part 5.B of this Section).

C. GEIGER COUNTERS*

The Geiger counter once was the most popular type of radiation detector, since it was capable of detecting any ionizing radiation with adequate sensitivity, and because of its large pulse size, it did not require a high-gain amplifier. Now, however, Geiger counters are not often used in laboratory counting for a number of reasons: their plateaus have a greater slope than proportional counters, and so a Geiger counting setup is not as stable as the proportional type; they possess a long dead time which arises from the mechanism of the discharge and cannot be reduced; finally, they produce a pulse of constant amplitude regardless of the initial ionization, and therefore cannot distinguish between alpha and beta particles. Geiger counters can be made into very rugged assemblies, and because they require only very simple ancillary equipment, they are widely used for survey devices and other field applications.

In general appearance the Geiger counters resemble their relatives, the proportional counters, but they differ in the nature of the filling gas and the pressure. Design requirements for a Geiger counter are rather critical, and a cylindrical geometry is almost always used because the necessary parameters are easily controlled.

Mechanism of the Geiger Counter. As mentioned earlier, in Part 4.A, if the voltage applied to a proportional counter is increased, all pulses eventually become of the same high amplitude, regardless of the initial

* See references 48, 133, 185, and 235.

ionization (see Fig. 61). This region of operation is called the Geiger region, and will be discussed briefly. Detailed treatments of the subject have been given by Wilkinson (235) and by Korff (133).

Just as in a proportional counter, the electrons drift toward the anode and become accelerated in the electric field. Their high energy enables them to release more electrons by ionization, each new electron releasing further ionization. Some of the excited atoms emit photons, and occasionally a photoelectron is produced. As the electric field strength increases, the number of photons produced in an avalanche grows until each avalanche produces a photoelectron. Since a single electron can start a new avalanche, the avalanche region spreads until it envelops the entire central wire.

As in a proportional counter, collection of all the electrons is a fast but small contribution to the voltage pulse. The larger part comes from electrostatic induction by the positive ion sheath as it crosses the high-field region on its way to the cathode.

If a positively charged rare-gas ion strikes the cathode, a secondary electron may be produced. This additional electron will result in another discharge unless provision is made to prevent multiple discharges by *quenching*. Almost all modern Geiger tubes are self-quenching; that is, they contain some polyatomic gas which brings a halt to the process when the positive ion sheath reaches the cathode. Argon-filled Geiger tubes frequently use alcohol as the quenching gas; in such a tube, an argon ion makes frequent collisions with argon atoms and alcohol molecules on its way to the cathode. The probability is very high that an argon ion will be neutralized in an encounter with an alcohol molecule, but the opposite transfer of charge is not energetically possible. Therefore, the positive ion sheath which finally reaches the cathode is composed only of alcohol molecular ions. These ions cannot release secondary electrons; instead, they become neutralized at the cathode surface and dissociate harmlessly. The organic gas eventually becomes depleted after about 10^9 counts have occurred, and the counter is no longer usable. The consumption of quenching gas increases with operating voltage.

The life of Geiger counters has been extended greatly through the use of halogens as quenching gas. A common filling is about 0.1% chlorine in neon. The quenching mechanism is the same as just described for organics, except that after the diatomic chlorine molecules dissociate at the cathode, they eventually recombine; thus, the quenching gas is continually replenished. This makes it possible to operate the tube at very high voltages without harm, and so very large signal pulses are obtainable.

Plateaus. The counting rate–voltage plateaus for Geiger counters do not, as a rule, have a very small slope. The organically quenched tubes

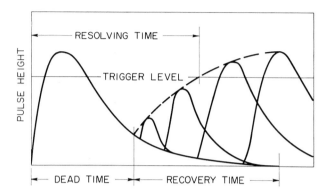

Fig. 67. Illustration of pulse shapes in a typical Geiger tube operating at a high counting rate. The dead time and recovery times are determined by the Geiger tube characteristics, but the resolving time depends on the triggering level of the electronic recording system.

exhibit plateaus 200–300 V long, with a slope of 1–2% per 100 v. Because of the organic quenching gas, their life is limited to only about 10^9 counts, and therefore should not be subjected to high counting rates for extended periods. The halogen-quenched tubes are characterized by shorter plateaus (100–200 V), and steeper slopes of 3–4% per 100 V. Halogen-quenched tubes have a much longer counting life, extending to perhaps 10^{11} counts. An early objection to the halogen-quenched tubes was that, because of the large anode used, the detection efficiency was not uniform over the window area. Recent improvements in design have largely eliminated this effect, and have improved the plateau performance to the extent quoted above.

Resolving Time.   Although the time constant of the counting equipment may be made quite short so only the initial part of the output pulse is utilized, the Geiger tube does not immediately recover from the discharge. Unlike the proportional counter, the positive ions form a nearly cylindrical sheath around the anode, which profoundly disrupts the electric field and prevents the initiation of new avalanches near the anode. This situation prevails until the ion sheath has migrated out of the high-field region. The time interval during which the tube is completely insensitive to additional ionizing particles is called the *dead time;* the time interval which follows is called the *recovery time*, because once the tube begins to count again, it requires a considerable period before the pulse size regains the original amplitude. This is illustrated in Figure 67.

In a practical measuring system, it is necessary to know the *resolving time*, or average time interval for which the recording equipment is insensitive. For a system which has the sensitivity to count all pulses, the resolving time will be equal to the dead time. Figure 67 shows that a system which triggers on high-amplitude pulses will exhibit a resolving time greater than the dead time. Typical dead times for Geiger tubes are from 100 to 300 μsec.

Corrections applied to counting data because of the resolving time are especially large and, therefore, important when using Geiger tubes. A precise value for the resolving time of a particular tube can only be determined by experiment. Such a determination can be made by using the multiple-source comparison method (131). Another method which offers some advantages is to count repeatedly a sample of some short-lived nuclide as it decays from a high rate to a very low rate. The known half-life may be fitted accurately to the points at low rates, for which the corrections are small or negligible, and the decay curve is extrapolated to time zero. The differences between the decay curve and the experimental points may be used to construct a correction curve directly, or to compute the resolving time.

The uncertainties in applying a resolving time correction may be avoided by fixing the resolving time of the detection system electronically at a value somewhat greater than the Geiger tube dead time.

Once the resolving time τ is known, the corrected counting rate R_0 can be approximated for any measured rate R, by

$$R_0 = R/(1 - R\tau) \tag{46}$$

The time unit for τ, R, and R_0 must be the same.

5. Auxiliary Electronic Instrumentation

A. GENERAL INTRODUCTION

So far, this section has been concerned with the detectors used in a nuclear measurement system. From time to time it has seemed advisable to remark upon some of the considerations which are important in selecting the electronic accessories to be used with a particular detector. The ensuing discussion will be devoted to a more general treatment of some of the available electronic equipment. We will not treat these devices in detail, but rather we will try to describe their nature and application so that an experimenter will be guided to select the measuring system best suited to his needs.

A nuclear measuring system capable of performing a variety of tasks is diagrammed in Figure 68. If *integral counting* is the only requirement, the pulse-height selector may be set to produce an output pulse for every input pulse whose amplitude exceeds a desired value. The scaler may record the number of pulses in a standard time interval, or the counting-rate meter may be used to indicate continuously the average counting rate. Should the experiment require data on the pulse-height distribution, the amplifier signals are fed to a pulse-height analyzer, for sorting and information storage.

Before describing the various components themselves, it may be noted that transistorized electronic devices are now available which are essentially equivalent to equipment using vacuum tubes; thus, linear amplifiers, scalers, and pulse-height analyzers generally may be obtained in either

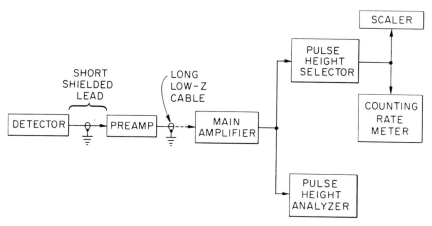

Fig. 68. Typical nuclear measuring system, with provisions either for integral counting or differential pulse-height analysis.

transistorized or vacuum-tube versions. On the basis of experience to date, it appears that transistorized units are to be preferred, even though they may be considerably more expensive in some cases. The chief advantage of transistor circuits is their greater reliability, and thus less need of maintenance, a particular benefit for laboratories not equipped with extensive repair facilities. Other advantages of transistors are small physical size and low heat dissipation.

B. AMPLIFIERS*

The signal from a radiation detector is produced by delivering an amount of charge q onto an input capacitance C. Typical values for the output voltages (given by q/C) from several detectors are listed in Table VIII. It is readily seen that the pulse heights obtained are very small, and so an amplifier is needed between the detector and measuring apparatus. For spectrometry, where a precision analysis of the pulse-height distribution is to be made, vacuum-tube amplifiers with positive output pulses of 0–100

* See references 44, 63, 66, and 86.

TABLE VIII
DETECTOR PULSE CHARACTERISTICS

Detector	Typical output signal[a]	Energy dependent	Rise time
Geiger-Müller	0–10 V	No	Slow
Proportional	0–100 mV	Yes	Slow
Pulse ion chamber	0–3 mV	Yes	Slow
Semiconductor	0–25 mV	Yes	Fast
Scintillation	0–2 V	Yes	Fast

[a] For a circuit capacitance of 20 picofarads.

V are often used; by contrast, transistorized amplifiers generally produce negative output pulses in the range 0–10 V.

To accommodate a wide range of detector operating conditions, vacuum-tube amplifiers for scintillation and proportional counters commonly have a maximum gain of 5000 to 50,000, with attenuators for setting the gain over a range of at least a factor of 100. Transistorized amplifiers require a voltage gain only about 0.1 as great.

The word amplifier as used here will be taken to mean a *linear amplifier*, i.e., one whose output amplitude is quite accurately proportional to the input amplitude. However, there are counting applications where nonlinear operation may be desired if the particular amplitude dependence can be kept reproducible and stable.

Pulse Shaping. The generalized detector waveform shown in Figure 69a defines the terms often used to describe such pulses. The rise time t_r depends on the particular detector; for example, the rise time of a scintillation detector pulse depends on the decay time of the fluorescent light and the photomultiplier characteristics. The fall time t_f of the pulse depends on the load resistance R and the capacitance C of the signal lead to ground: $t_f = 2.2\,RC$.

Usually the fall time must be quite long relative to the rise time; this leads to the situation sketched in Figure 69b, which shows the pulses appearing at the input of an amplifier, all with the same characteristic fall time. Because of the high rate, the "tail" of one pulse does not decay to the base line before another pulse appears. Such a state of affairs will not permit an accurate pulse-height analysis to be made. Further, since the useful information is contained in the leading edge of the pulse and its top, the tail only complicates the problem to no purpose.

The desired early portion of the detector pulse is extracted by using a *clipping*, or *differentiating* circuit (66, 129). Several electrical networks will perform the mathematical operation of differentiation; the most obvious

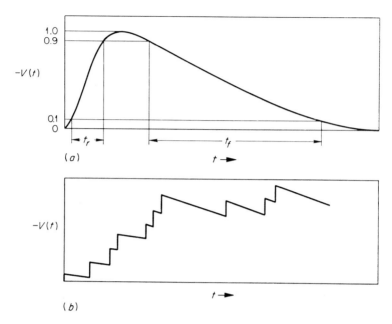

Fig. 69. Radiation detector pulses. (*a*) Single pulse plotted on an expanded scale to show definitions of rise time t_r, and fall time, t_f. (*b*) Pulses appearing at the input of an amplifier. All pulses have the same fast rise time, followed by a slow fall time. The high pulse rate causes the pulses to sum.

approach is to use a single coupling stage in the amplifier whose RC product (or *time constant*) is much less than the others. This system suffers from two defects: there is a signal present in the amplifier long after the peak is reached (Fig. 70*a*), even though the fall time now is about 100 times faster than for the detector pulse; therefore, the clipping is not complete. In addition, practical amplifiers have many stages and so there are, in effect, many differentiating circuits. An analysis shows that when only one RC time constant is short, every output pulse will be followed by a low-amplitude signal of opposite polarity (*undershoot*), which lasts for a very long time, and whose area equals the area of the signal pulse. If additional pulses are processed during the recovery from an undershoot, the amplitude of such signals may be seriously altered. Further, the average voltage or *baseline* will no longer be zero, but will vary with changes in counting rate.

Clearly, it is desirable to reduce the duration of the undershoot so that the probability of pulse overlap is small. If two time constants in the amplifier are equal to each other and are smaller than those of the remaining networks, then the undershoot will have the largest amplitude and the

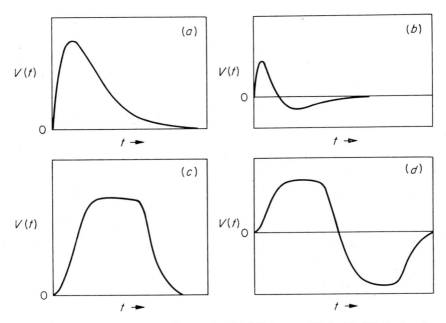

Fig. 70. Output pulses from amplifiers using (a) *RC* clipping, (b) double *RC* clipping, (c) single delay-line clipping, and (d) double delay-line clipping.

shortest duration. This pulse shaping is known as *double differentiation,* or *double clipping;* a typical waveform is shown in Figure 70b. Although the areas under the main pulse and its undershoot are equal under the conditions of Figure 70b, the amplitudes are not. As a result, there may be serious difficulties if the amplifier is driven out of its linear range by very large detector pulses. For example, when the amplifier is set for high gain in order to study low-energy radiation, then high-energy pulses which are also detected will drive the amplifier to its saturation output value. Under this *overload* condition, it is unlikely that the undershoot will be distorted in the same way as the main pulse, and so at high counting rates, baseline shifts can still occur.

Clipping with a delay line is to be preferred over the *RC* clipping techniques just described. An example of an amplifier which uses a shorted delay line clipper (with provisions for *RC* clipping if desired) is the Oak Ridge National Laboratory model A1D, designed by Bell, Kelley, and Goss, and described in reference 186; the A1D output wave form is sketched in Figure 70c. The advantages of delay-line clipping over *RC* clipping are: (a) the pulse is almost rectangular, and so the long tail characteristic of *RC* clipping is eliminated; and (b) the top of the pulse is more nearly flat, a desirable circumstance when certain types of pulse-height analyzers are to be employed. A disadvantage is that the delay-line circuits often used give rise to a small undershoot, which causes a baseline shift at high counting rates.

The best pulse shape for most work is obtained by double clipping with delay lines. The symmetry of such a pulse, shown in Figure 70d, leads to excellent overload and counting rate properties, since the area balance between positive and negative halves is essentially unchanged by overload. Double differentiation as a means of pulse shaping in a linear amplifier was proposed by E. Fairstein and R. A. Dandl. Practical applications of this technique are the Oak Ridge amplifiers model DD-2 (67), and the model A-8 (122). A transistorized design by Goulding et al. (90) has recently appeared.

The overload performance of an amplifier is extremely important in modern experiments, where it may be necessary to study low-energy radiations in the presence of a high-energy background. For example, the gain of an amplifier may be set so that maximum output is obtained for 50 keV of energy detected; if 5-MeV detector pulses are also present, they are said to drive the amplifier to 100 times overload. Such harsh treatment can lead to blocking, or a temporary amplifier paralysis following an overload pulse. Naturally, if high counting rates are to be tolerated, the amplifier should recover quickly after an overload. Double delay-line differentiation and careful attention to blocking make it possible for the A-8 to recover after a $4000 \times$ overload in less than 10 μsec., with no positive baseline excursion after the main pulse.

Noise. The extent to which amplifier noise is important will depend on the kind of measurement being made. If the amplifier is part of a simple counter, noise introduces spurious counts; thus, the lowest amplitude of usable signal is approximately equal to the noise level. If the amplifier is part of a spectrometer, the noise signals are not counted directly, but appear as a broadening influence on spectral lines. As mentioned in Section VI.3.C, the noise is often stated in energy units such as kilo electron volts (KeV) This is an experimenter's way of expressing the more fundamental noise unit, the *equivalent charge* (68), which is a convenient concept because nuclear detector signals consist of bursts of charge collected on the input capacitance. By using units of charge instead of voltage, the capacitance need not be known.

The main sources of noise in a well-designed amplifier are those arising from the thermal motion of electrons in the input grid resistor, and the noise from the input tube due to flicker effect, grid current, and shot effect. The last two of these are usually the dominant contributions. The general trend is that noise increases with input capacitance. For more details, the reader may consult the recent reviews by Fairstein (66,68) and the earlier book by Gillespie (86).

In a measuring system, sources of noise other than those associated with the amplifier must be evaluated. The photocathode of a photomultiplier tube releases electrons by thermal agitation which appear as random noise; if a scintillation counter is to be useful at low energies (and, therefore, low light intensities), this source of noise is usually far more important than the amplifier noise. At present, noise from the leakage current of a semiconductor radiation detector, rather than amplifier noise, limits the energy resolution of this device.

The noise problem becomes acute when an amplifier must be used for spectrometry with detectors of low output amplitude, but with high energy resolution. Examples of this case would be a semiconductor radiation detector or pulse ionization chamber. These detectors usually are not required to accommodate a large range of signal amplitudes, so overload performance is not very critical. An analysis shows that these conditions can best be satisfied with single RC clipping, if the counting rates are not very high. Double differentiation gives a relatively higher noise contribution, but may be justified if the counting rates are to be high.

Scintillation detectors produce large signals (see Table VIII), but exhibit rather poor resolution. Therefore, the slight worsening of the noise level by double differentiation is negligible. On the other hand, the wide range of detector signal amplitudes requires double differentiation to achieve good overload characteristics.

Presently available transistors cannot equal the low noise performance of vacuum tubes at low input capacitances. With input capacitances of 15–20 picofarads, transistor amplifiers exhibit 3–10 times more noise than the best vacuum tube amplifiers. At input capacitances of about 1000 picofarads, the two systems are equal (64). The poorer noise level for transistor amplifiers, while serious in the most critical high-resolution applications, is well within the acceptable limits for NaI(Tl) scintillation spectrometry.

Window Amplifiers. In many experiments it may not be desirable to cover the energy range starting at zero. For example, alpha particles from heavy nuclides all have energies greater than about 4 MeV, and thus some way of shifting the amplifier threshold is indicated. This is accomplished by first amplifying the pulses in the usual way, and then subtracting a constant amount of height from each pulse. The resulting pulses then are amplified to the required size by an amplifier with good overload properties. Such output amplifiers are variously known as *expander amplifiers, window amplifiers*, or more recently, as *post amplifiers*. This technique, especially as regards its application in improving the precision of pulse-height analyzers, is reviewed by Van Rennes (223); some considerations based on recent developments in alpha spectroscopy were discussed by Fairstein (68). The Oak Ridge model Q-2069 amplifier system (143) is a good example of a low-noise amplifier for alpha spectrometry, and includes a convenient post amplifier arrangement.

Preamplifiers. An amplifier system usually is divided into a preamplifier and the main amplifier (Fig. 68). It is undesirable to couple the detector to a voltage-sensitive amplifier through a long cable because of the attendant signal losses and the increase in noise level associated with high cable capacitance. The use of a preamplifier mounted on or near the detector makes it possible to provide the shortest possible detector leads. A preamplifier may have a gain ranging from 1 to 30, and should have as its output stage a cathode follower capable of driving long sections of low-impedance cable, such as 93-ohm RG-62/U, with good linearity. This permits the detector and preamplifier to be located 500 feet or more from the complex of measuring equipment with good results.

As was stressed earlier, nuclear particle detectors produce a packet of charge. Until recently, all preamplifiers were of the voltage-sensitive type, i.e., the output pulse height is proportional to q/C. However, it is now realized that a charge-sensitive amplifier is to be preferred in most applications. Since the output is essentially proportional to q alone, the pulse height does not vary with input capacitance, as has already been mentioned in connection with semiconductor radiation detectors (Section VI.3.C). Therefore, the experimenter is able to alter the input circuit and still retain approximately the same gain calibration. It is not necessary to compromise on noise specifications, since for the same input capacitance as for a voltage-sensitive amplifier, the charge-sensitive device exhibits nearly the same noise contribution. In view of its convenience, it is likely that most new preamplifiers will be of the charge-sensitive type.

C. TRIGGER CIRCUITS

Nuclear detection systems make frequent use of devices known as *trigger circuits*, which produce a pulse of constant height and width for each incoming pulse whose height exceeds a set value. A trigger which is adjusted by a front panel control is called an integral *pulse-height selector* (PHS) or *integral discriminator*. As shown in Figure 68, it may be used to produce pulses of standard height for operating a scaler or counting-rate meter. Also, a PHS is needed in most integral counting work for discrimination against amplifier noise, or low-amplitude pulses from unwanted radiations.

D. SCALERS

It is essential that a counting system be capable of accurate counting at high rates. Electromechanical registers can only accommodate counting rates up to 60 per second, while many experiments demand recording data at rates of 30,000 counts per second or more. This is accomplished by

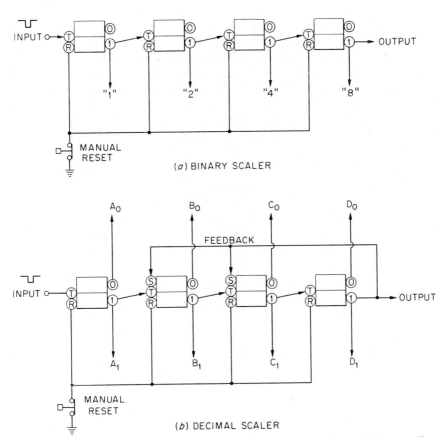

Fig. 71. Functional diagram of scalers. (*a*) A cascade of four binaries, yielding a scaling factor of 16. (*b*) A scaler made up of four binaries wired for decimal counting.

dividing the number of incoming pulses by a known factor (the scaling factor), so that a register will follow the reduced rate. The electronic device for performing this division is called a *scaler*.

The simplest high-speed scaling device is the scale-of-2, often called a *binary*, because it is a circuit having two stable states representing the binary numbers 0 and 1. The first input pulse transfers the state from 0 to 1; the second event will reset the binary to the 0 state, and also generate an output, or *carry* pulse. Thus, only one output pulse is produced for two input pulses, so for a series of n such stages, a scaling factor of 2^n is obtained.

An array of four binaries in cascade to give a scale-of-16 is shown in Figure 71*a*. Each stage is connected to an indicator such as a lamp, which functions when the stage is switched to the 1 state. In Figure 71*a*, the first pulse causes the lamp labeled "1" to light. The second pulse resets the first binary to 0 and sets the second binary to 1; this has the effect of extinguishing the "1" lamp and lighting the "2" lamp. A third pulse causes the "1" lamp to light also; a fourth will extinguish these but will light the "4" lamp, and so on until 15 events have been recorded and all lamps are lighted (1 + 2 + 4 + 8 = 15). The next pulse resets all binary stages, extinguishing the indicator lamps, and produces a carry pulse at the output. This latter pulse can be used to drive a register, or further binaries.

When many binary stages are connected in cascade to form a large electronic register, it becomes tedious for the experimenter to translate the binary information into decimal form. Obviously, it is desirable to employ decimal scalers wherever possible. Improvements in electronic components and circuitry during the past few years have made it possible to construct decimal scalers which are as reliable as the binary ones.

A functional diagram for a transistorized decimal scaling stage usable to a pulse rate of 1 Mc. is shown in Figure 71b. It is composed of four binaries and a "feedback" circuit to modify the scale-of-16 to a scale-of-10 as follows: The first seven counts are recorded as described above for a binary scaler; on the eighth count, the last binary switches to indicate an "8," but also a short pulse is fed to the second and third binaries, setting up a "2" and a "4," respectively. Thus, on the eighth count the binaries are switched as though 14 (2 + 4 + 8) counts had been received. The ninth count records normally, and on the tenth all binaries are reset and a carry pulse emerges from the output.

The leads A_0, A_1, B_0, B_1, etc., sense the state of each binary, and may be used to indicate the number of stored counts. However, indicators cannot be connected directly to these leads; unlike the binary scaler, a translating circuit is required. For visual presentation and automatic recording on punched cards, it is useful to translate the information into decimal form, i.e., the digits 0–9; however, for many automatic recording systems, it is more economical to employ *binary-coded decimal* (BCD) format, in which the numbers 0–9 are expressed either as combinations of the digits, 1, 2, 4, and 8, or 1, 2, 4, and 2′. Sometimes the decimal code is called a "10-line" format, and the BCD is called a "4-line" format.

Other reliable decade scalers have been devised and are in everyday use. The cold-cathode, glow-discharge scaler tubes made by several manufacturers (Ericsson Telephone Company, Sylvania Electric Products Company, and Raytheon Manufacturing Company) are capable of operation between 20 and 100 kc. The electron beam-switching tubes made by the Burroughs Corporation will function above 1 Mc. Often a beam-switching tube is used as a high-speed scaling stage, followed by a series of glow tubes. The operation and use of some of these devices have been described by Millman and Taub (150).

E. COUNTING-RATE METERS

It is extremely convenient to be able to measure the counting rate continuously, without the necessity of counting with a scaler for a measured amount of time. A device which indicates continuously the average counting rate is called a *counting-rate meter*. This is the indicator most often used on portable survey instruments.

Most counting-rate meters exhibit a linear relationship between output and counting rate. This is obtained by coupling a pulse of constant amplitude from a pulse-height selector onto a "tank," or storage, capacitor which is shunted by a resistor. Each pulse transfers a known charge to the tank capacitor; the steady-state voltage developed across the tank capacitor is reached when the rate of charge loss through the shunt resistor equals the rate of charge input from the pulses. A good quality vacuum-tube voltmeter is used to indicate the voltage across the *RC* tank circuit. Linear counting-rate meters have been discussed by Elmore and Sands (63) and by Price (186).

When wide ranges of counting rate must be measured, a logarithmic response is desirable. Usually this is done by using a logarithmic vacuum-tube voltmeter to read the voltage. It is very difficult to achieve very high accuracy or stability with such a technique, although adequate logarithmic counting-rate meters have been designed for survey purposes. Price (186) has reviewed the various approaches to this problem.

F. PULSE-HEIGHT ANALYZERS

Several of the detectors used in nuclear studies yield pulses whose heights depend on the energy deposited in the detector. This suggests that if these energy-dependent pulses can be sorted according to their height, energy spectra can be obtained. The device for performing this sorting is usually called a *pulse-height analyzer*.

A simple illustration of the problem is shown in Figure 72: In Figure 72a, a series of pulses from a detector is viewed very much as it would appear as a voltage–time waveform on an oscilloscope. The example shows the pulse-height scale divided into five channels of equal width. Over the counting interval shown, a 5-channel pulse-height analyzer would record no events in channels 1 and 5, two events in channels 2 and 4, and five events in channel 3. Thus, the data from such an analysis may be plotted as the histogram shown in Figure 72b; usually, it is more convenient to plot the number of events per channel as a point at each channel number. A smooth curve drawn through these experimental points is easier to interpret.

Single-Channel Analyzers. The number of events shown in Figure 72 is, of course, a ridiculously small sample of a random source of pulses. Al-

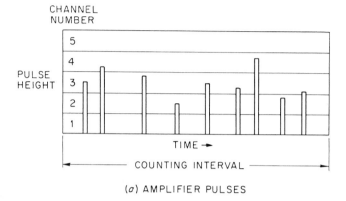

(a) AMPLIFIER PULSES

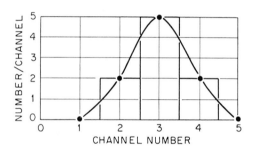

(b) PULSE-HEIGHT DISTRIBUTION

Fig. 72. Illustration of the pulse-height analysis problem. (a) Idealized pulses from a linear amplifier are shown, plotted on a pulse-height scale which is divided into five equal channels. (b) The pulse-height distribution from (a) is shown plotted as a smooth curve through the points.

though it is more efficient to record the events in all channels at once, it requires only very simple equipment to look through an electronic "window" at a single portion of the spectrum at a time. The window might be adjusted to the width of a channel in Figure 72a, and set to the position of each channel shown. At each setting, a count would be taken for a sufficient length of time to obtain a valid statistical sample of the spectrum. The data may be plotted as in Figure 72b.

The operation of such a single-channel pulse-height analyzer is simple in principle, although fairly complex in practice. Figure 73 shows the general arrangement and mode of operation for three pulses. Two pulse-height selector (PHS) units are used: a lower PHS is biased to trigger on a pulse of height E, and an upper PHS biased to $E + \Delta E$. The anticoincidence circuit will permit an output pulse only if the lower PHS is triggered without a pulse from the upper PHS. The E dial in the case shown is set at 200 dial divisions; pulse "1" does not have sufficient amplitude to affect either

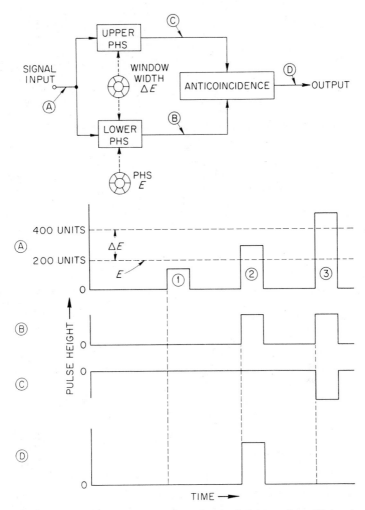

Fig. 73. Functional diagram of a single-channel pulse-height analyzer. Pulse shapes for the different part of the circuit are shown below the block diagram.

PHS. Pulse "2" falls within the ΔE window, which causes the lower PHS to trigger; as there is no accompanying pulse from the upper PHS, an output pulse is recorded. The third pulse is high enough to trigger both PHS units, so the anticoincidence circuit prevents an output.

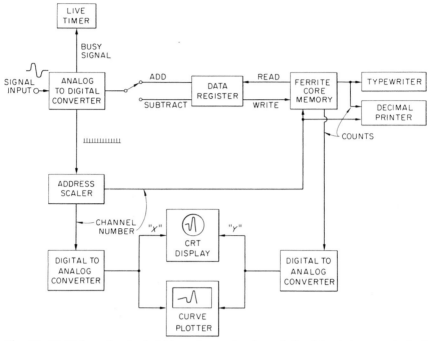

Fig. 74. Multichannel pulse-height analyzer, showing relationships between principal subassemblies and accessory equipment.

Several versions of vacuum-tube single-channel analyzers have been described [see, for example, the reviews by Chase (44) and Van Rennes (223)]. Transistorized versions are also in use which are compatible with the transistorized linear amplifiers (43,91).

Multichannel Analyzers. Many applications require faster data acquisition rates than are possible with single-channel analyzers. A notable example is found in the field of radioactivation analysis, where it has become increasingly important to measure short-lived nuclides for highest sensitivity (cf., Section II.1.B). Not only is there a great increase in speed and convenience if the pulses are sorted in a single counting interval, but there is also an improvement in the precision of the data obtained because many instrumental drifts will affect all channels of a *multichannel pulse-height analyzer* in the same way. For circuits used in these instruments, the reader is directed to the recent discussion by Chase (44), and the earlier review edited by Koch and Johnston (128).

The most obvious approach to the design of a multichannel analyzer is to construct a number of pulse-height selectors, whose trigger (or bias) levels are progressively increased. Anticoincidence circuitry is provided, so that, in effect, the array consists of a series of single-channel analyzers, "stacked up" in terms of pulse height. A successful version of this scheme is the 20-channel analyzer designed by Bell, Kelley, and Goss. This analyzer, together with a review of the general problem of pulse-height analysis, is discussed by Van Rennes (223).

Improvements in detector resolution and the growing need for more automated data recording have created a need for multichannel analyzers with a very large number of channels. The 20-channel analyzer just mentioned cost about \$350/channel; hence, a stacked-discriminator type of analyzer is too expensive to build in large configurations. By making use of techniques developed for digital computers, it is possible to construct multichannel analyzers having hundreds of channels, and very large storage capacities per channel. A simplified diagram illustrating the general method of operation of such an analyzer, as well as some of the methods of handling the data, is sketched in Figure 74.

The heart of the analyzer is the *analog-to-digital converter* (ADC), which converts the pulse height to a train of pulses. The number of pulses produced determines the channel number in which the pulse is to be stored. These *address* pulses are counted by the *address scaler*, which may be either a binary or a binary-coded decimal (BCD) type.

The information is stored in a ferrite-core *memory* unit, which resembles the memory of a modern digital computer. The memory usually stores data in BCD format, as this is most useful for operating readout equipment. Some of the early instruments used all binary logic, which is more economical but a little more troublesome for the experimenter. Once the address scaler has selected a memory address (channel number), the number of counts already stored in the memory at that address is read out into a scaler called the *data register*, or *add-one-scaler*. Then, the store command is given, the data register increases the old number by one, and the new number is written back into the memory. This *memory cycle* requires 10–20 μsec. for most analyzers.

Analysis of a pulse-height distribution in this way requires a rather long time. A typical analyzer might have an 18-μsec. memory cycle and a 0.5-μsec. spacing between address pulses (2-Mc. address pulse rate); this leads to an analysis time for each pulse (during which the analyzer is incapable of recording any further pulses) of $(18 + 0.5\nu)$ μsec., where ν is the channel number.

The dependence of the rather long "dead time" on channel number shows that the average dead time is a function of the spectrum under measurement. However, it can be shown that the spectrum shape is undistorted under this condition, and so it is only necessary to correct for the dead time to obtain accurate counting rates. Instead of working with dead time, it is more convenient to count for a given amount of "live time," that is, time during which the analyzer is free to analyze incoming pulses. The device for measuring live time, a *live timer*, is an electronic clock which counts standard-frequency pulses; when the analyzer is processing a count, the ADC produces a *busy signal*, which stops the clock. Therefore, only live time is recorded.

Because the analyzer operates on computer principles, it has the ability to subtract as well as add. It is quite helpful to subtract background spectra using the analyzer. Some commercially available analyzers have provisions for storing a spectrum in one part of the memory; the intensity of this spectrum may be multiplied by normalizing factors and then added or subtracted from the contents of another portion of the memory.

A variety of readout equipment is possible. The decimal numbers may be recorded by using a typewriter or printer; BCD information may be recorded in computer format on punched paper tape or on magnetic tape. Digital information also may be converted to analog voltages, which are used to display spectra on a cathode-ray tube, and may also be used to drive an X-Y curve plotter.

G. COINCIDENCE MEASUREMENTS

In many nuclear counting problems, it is necessary to decide whether two events are time-correlated. Such information may be required for investigations of nuclear decay schemes (Section II.3), where it may be necessary to know whether two radiations are emitted at the same time. Also in many types of counting, imposing the condition that two events must be coincident in time will serve to discriminate effectively against noise pulses that are randomly distributed in time. Electronic circuits which make such decisions are called *coincidence* circuits, and produce an output pulse only if all inputs to the device receive a pulse simultaneously.

Coincidence equipments may be classified according to their *resolving time*. If a two-channel system is used, each channel applies a gate pulse of width τ to the mixer circuit; therefore, to be in coincidence, the two gate pulses must fall within the time interval 2τ, the resolving time. A resolving time of less than a few tenths of a microsecond is termed "fast," and longer resolving times are called "slow." With special-purpose photomultiplier tubes and high-speed circuitry, resolving times of less than 10^{-9} sec. (1 nanosec.) have been obtained. The esoteric subject of fast coincidence measurements will not be treated here, but has been reviewed extensively by De Benedetti and Findley (56) and by Lewis and Wells (139). Resolving times of >50 nanosec. are possible, however, with rather conventional equipment.

Short resolving times are required wherever high counting rates are involved, because the random nature of radioactive decay leads to a chance that two uncorrelated pulses will happen to occur within the coincidence resolving time. The random coincidence rate N_r is given by

$$N_r = 2\tau \, \mathbf{R_1 R_2} \tag{47}$$

where $\mathbf{R_1}$ and $\mathbf{R_2}$ are the counting rates in the two channels. Note that, because $\mathbf{R_1}$ and $\mathbf{R_2}$ are related to the disintegration rate N_D by efficiencies ϵ_1 and ϵ_2, the random coincidence rate is proportional to the square of the disintegration rate:

$$N_r = 2\tau \, N_D{}^2 \, \epsilon_1 \epsilon_2 \tag{48}$$

A criterion for feasibility of a coincidence experiment is the ratio of real coincidences to random coincidences. Since the real coincident rate is given by

$$N_c = N_D \, \epsilon_1 \epsilon_2$$

then,

$$N_c/N_r = 1/(2\tau \, N_D) \tag{49}$$

Thus, the real-to-random ratio increases only as the reciprocal of the resolving time and disintegration rate to the first power.

A block diagram of a typical coincidence system is given in Figure 75. The coincidence circuit requires that, to be quantitative, the timing pulses should not "walk," i.e., change their position in time as the pulse height varies. The output from the usual trigger circuits will exhibit such a walk, because low-amplitude pulses will trigger near their peaks, while high-amplitude pulses will trigger proportionately nearer the baseline. The output pulses will be distributed through a time range about equal to the amplifier rise time (~ 0.2 μsec. for NaI(Tl) scintillation detectors). A convenient solution to this problem was proposed by Love, who pointed out that the crossover point (point A in Fig. 75) of the pulse from an amplifier with double delay-line differentiation (Part 5.B of this section) showed negligible walk with pulse height, since the point is only determined by the delay-line parameters. Several timing circuits based on this idea have been constructed by Peele and Love (175), and Fairstein (69). Transistorized versions of such a system have also been designed (43, 91).

All pulses are subjected to a fast coincidence ($2\tau = 0.1$ μsec.) in Figure 75. Then, if coincidence measurements are desired between two energy bands, these are selected by the two single-channel pulse-height analyzers. Thus, of all the integral coincidences recorded by the fast unit, only a few will be selected by the analyzers. The slow coincidence unit, which may

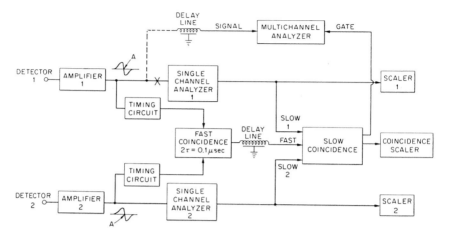

Fig. 75. Coincidence apparatus. For use with a multichannel analyzer, the connection to single-channel analyzer 1 is broken at ×, and the connection shown as a
dotted line is used.

have a resolving time of 2–5 μsec., imposes these additional pulse-height
conditions. As a result of this arrangement, the resolving time of the system is determined by the fast coincidence; the relatively low rates and less
sharply timed signals from the single-channel analyzers can be mixed
quite accurately with the fast coincidence output in a slow coincidence
unit.

Often, it is desirable to include a multichannel analyzer in a coincidence
arrangement, in order to measure the spectrum at one detector in coincidence with a selected energy from another detector. As shown in Figure
75, the connection to single-channel analyzer 1 is broken and a slow coincidence is demanded only between the "Fast" and "Slow 2" channels.
With the multichannel analyzer connected to amplifier 1, a coincidence
between detector 1 and a count in the window of single-channel analyzer 2
will supply a gate signal which commands the multichannel analyzer
to record the pulse appearing at its input.

A related technique makes use of a signal which inhibits the multi-
channel analyzer or other apparatus from recording particular events.
One application of this *anticoincidence* arrangement is discussed below in
Part 6.

Coincidence techniques are well suited to the measurements of very
short half-lives. If delay lines are inserted between the timing circuit and
fast-coincidence input, first in one channel and then the other, a *delay
curve* can be obtained, which is just the coincidence counting rate as a function of added delay. This curve will have a width at half-maximum count-

ing rate of 2τ, if the two radiations are prompt: however, should one of the radiations be delayed, the delay curve will be steep on one side, but will exhibit a smaller slope on the other side, The analysis of such data to obtain lifetimes of nuclear states is discussed in references 56 and 10.

6. Low-Level Counting

A. GENERAL REMARKS

Many chemical experiments lead to very small amounts of radioactive sample, either because of the low yield of the reaction under study, or because of the small amount of sample available. It may be found that if a conventional detector is used for counting such low-intensity samples, the sample counting rate is comparable to the background sources.

When choosing between detector systems, the criterion for optimum counting precision in a given time is the "figure of merit" $R_S{}^2/R_B$, where R_S is the sample counting rate and R_B is the background rate (2). The system which gives the largest figure of merit is the most sensitive for the measurement of a particular nuclide. Therefore, the reduction in the background rate must be large in order to be effective, since the sample counting rate appears to the second power and the background only as the first. Increasing the sample counting rate by improvement of geometry, reduction of absorption, or some other means is far more valuable. The other practical criterion for low-level counting is stability, because a single determination may extend over days or weeks.

Detectors used for low-level counting are similar to the ones already discussed but differ in their application. The choice of a particular detector, which must be considered separately from the various ways of reducing the background, will depend upon the specific activity of the material to be counted. When the specific activity is low, as in radiocarbon dating, there is no point in considering a method that will not permit introducing a large sample and counting with high efficiency. The beta-particle energy is also involved in the choice of a detector, since absorption effects in the sample and counter window are extremely acute for beta particles below about 200 keV. On the other hand, absorption is a relatively minor consideration for high-energy beta particles.

The most difficult counting situation is encountered when the samples of interest combine a low specific activity with a low beta-particle energy. Typical samples of tritium (H^3) and C^{14} fall in this category. The usual techniques for low-level counting of these nuclides are gas counting and liquid scintillation counting.

The general problem of low-level counting has been reviewed by Arnold (2), Kulp (135), and DeVoe (59). The report by DeVoe (59) is especially valuable because of the wealth of information it contains about the radio-active contamination of materials needed by workers attempting to detect minimal amounts of radioactivity.

B. APPARATUS

Large-Volume Counters. A typical arrangement of a low-background, large-volume counter is shown in Figure 76a. The detector is situated at the center of a steel shield; lead is usually avoided because of its associated radioactivity. The mercury shield around the detector is to stop any radiation produced in the walls of the tubes comprising the anticoincidence mantle.

The most important single feature is the anticoincidence mantle; this device, although shown in the figure as a ring of Geiger tubes, may also be a hollow cylinder of scintillator, coupled to one or more photomultiplier tubes. An anticoincidence circuit uses the signal from the mantle to exclude events in which the detector and the mantle simultaneously produce a count, since an event in both detectors would indicate the detection of a particle from outside the source region. The anticoincidence ring may effect a reduction in the background of a beta-ray counter of about 50. The over-all reduction in background over a bare detector by the apparatus of Figure 76a is often between 100 and 150.

It is difficult to reduce the background of a large NaI(Tl) gamma-ray detector by using an anticoincidence mantle. In the energy region of 0–3 MeV, the background of such a gamma-ray detector may be reduced by a factor of only 2 to 5 through the use of a liquid or a plastic scintillator anticoincidence mantle. For the high-energy range above 3 MeV, in which the background is chiefly due to mesons, the background is reduced by a factor of 10^3–10^5 (177).

Small-Volume Counters. When the counter can be made very small, the experimental arrangement is much simpler. For instance, because the sensitive volume of a liquid scintillation counter can be so small, the shielding is often accomplished by a mercury shield so thick that an anticoincidence mantle is not required.

An end-window beta proportional counter of small dimensions will have a low background simply because its sensitive volume is small. If this small counter is placed inside a larger detector (Fig. 76b) and the two are placed in anticoincidence, a reduction in the background of at least a factor of 10 may be obtained. This entire assembly may be inserted into a massive shield for a further background reduction. The Omni/Guard detector manufactured by Tracer-lab, Inc., is designed in this way and has a background of < 0.5 counts per minute.

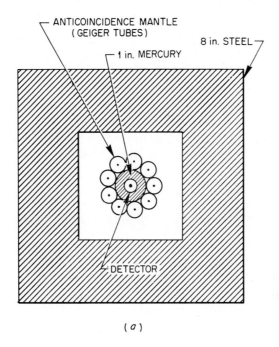

ANTICOINCIDENCE MANTLE
(GEIGER TUBES)

8 in. STEEL

1 in. MERCURY

DETECTOR

(a)

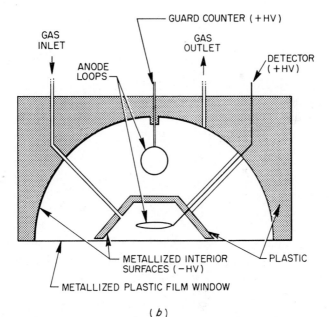

GUARD COUNTER (+ HV)

GAS
INLET

GAS
OUTLET

DETECTOR
(+ HV)

ANODE
LOOPS

METALLIZED INTERIOR
SURFACES (−HV)

PLASTIC

METALLIZED PLASTIC FILM WINDOW

(b)

Fig. 76. Low-background counters. (a) Typical arrangement for obtaining very low backgrounds. (b) Low-background proportional counter covered by an anticoincidence or guard counter.

167

7. Determination of the Disintegration Rate

In this Part, we will discuss the special techniques for determination of the disintegration rate, often called *absolute* counting, to distinguish it from relative counting procedures. Absolute counting may be performed directly as in $4\pi\beta$ counting; more often, absolute counting involves equipment normally employed for relative counting which has been calibrated by use of a standard source. For details of the techniques to be described, the reader may consult the excellent review by Steinberg (214), and proceedings of several conferences on this subject (174,188).

A. ABSOLUTE ALPHA COUNTING

General Considerations. Alpha particles have a short range in matter, so a good alpha source must be very thin (see Section III). By the same token, counter windows or other material through which the alpha particles must pass also should be thin; it is common to use windowless counters for such purposes.

Scattering in the sample itself is not a serious problem with alpha particles, since the particles scatter only slightly in thin sources. Scattering from the source mount is appreciable at small angles to the source plane, but is negligible at angles normal to the source plane. The amount of backscattering increases with the Z of the scatterer and with decreasing energy of the particles.

A variety of geometries are used. The usual one for moderate precision is the internal sample counter (a proportional counter or ionization chamber) with 2π geometry. Here, the backscattered particles are also counted, so the effective geometry for sources on polished platinum plates is found to be in the range 51–52%, depending on the energy. Work of the highest precision with sources on metal plates requires collimation to eliminate the backscattered particles; both low- and medium-geometry counters have been used very successfully. If the source to be standardized can be mounted on a thin, essentially weightless, film, then a 4π proportional counter may be used for accurate assay (144,169).

Many alpha sources must be counted in the presence of intense beta activities; therefore, it is essential that the detector and electronic system have a short resolving time, lest beta-induced pulses pile up and be counted as though they were alpha pulses. Fast detectors suitable for precision alpha counting are scintillation counters, semiconductor detectors, and proportional counters.

Low-Geometry Counters. When very accurate assays are required, or when the source intensity is very high, a low-geometry alpha counter is used. The general technique has been discussed by Curtis *et al.* (54) and Robinson (194).

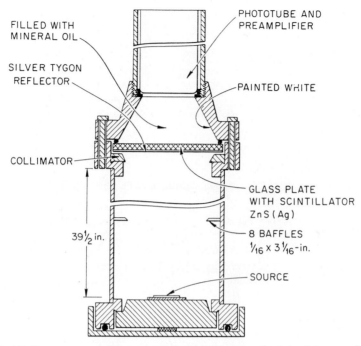

FILLED WITH
MINERAL OIL

SILVER TYGON
REFLECTOR

COLLIMATOR

39½ in.

PHOTOTUBE AND
PREAMPLIFIER

PAINTED WHITE

GLASS PLATE
WITH SCINTILLATOR
ZnS(Ag)

8 BAFFLES
1/16 x 3 1/16-in.

SOURCE

Fig. 77. Low-geometry alpha counter for high-precision absolute alpha counting
[Robinson (194)].

A design by Robinson (194) is shown in Figure 77. The chamber has a factor of about 1/2600 of 4π geometry. The chamber must be evacuated to a pressure of about 200 microns or less. Because the wall diameter is so near the collimator diameter, the eight baffles are required to prevent scattering particles off the walls and into the detector; without baffles, scattering amounts to about 1% of the total count. The high degree of collimation effectively eliminates backscattered particles from the source.

Many low-geometry chambers use a proportional counter as a detector, which requires a gas-tight window between it and the evacuated chamber. Some proportional counters also may require efficiency corrections because of the anode wire supports. The scintillation counter sketched in Figure 77 is free of these problems.

If all important dimensions are known to 1 part in 10,000, then the counting accuracy is mainly limited by statistics. The plateaus can be held flat to 0.05% with proper attention to the electronic equipment, and the influence of sample size on the geometry is not great because of the large distance between source and detector. As an example of the accuracy of the method, assays of the same sample by workers at the AERE, Harwell,

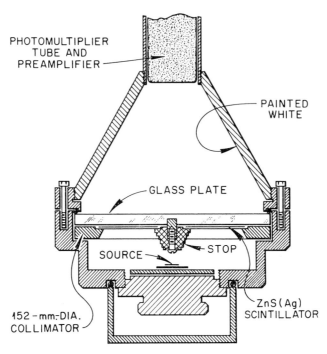

PHOTOMULTIPLIER
TUBE AND
PREAMPLIFIER

PAINTED
WHITE

GLASS PLATE

SOURCE   STOP

152-mm-DIA.
COLLIMATOR

ZnS(Ag)
SCINTILLATOR

Fig. 78. Precision high geometry alpha counter which uses a stop to reduce the effect of sample position on geometry (Robinson, in reference 188).

England, and LRL, Berkeley, California agreed within 0.1%, using low-geometry chambers of different design (89).

Precision, High-Geometry Counters. When the amount of activity to be assayed is small, it is necessary to use some sort of high-geometry configuration to obtain good counting statistics in a reasonable time. Although the 4π counter is a very attractive arrangement, the required source must be mounted on a nearly weightless backing. Most alpha sources are mounted on backing plates, for which the 4π method is not suitable. For relative counting it is quite suitable to use an internal sample counter with 2π geometry, for which the over-all efficiency, or *counting yield*, may be calibrated with standards if desired.

For absolute counting at high geometry, it is advisable to eliminate the backscattered alpha particles by reducing the geometry to about one π steradian, which leads to an acceptance angle of 120°. When this is done, the geometry factor becomes very sensitive to the size and position of the source.

This sensitivity to sample position is greatly improved by masking the detector of a high-geometry counter with a stop of the proper shape.

Figure 78 shows the design by Robinson (188). The chamber has a calculated geometry of 0.19748. A 2-mm. diameter source on platinum gave an essentially constant counting rate for displacements up to several millimeters from the center of the source holder. That this device is indeed a high-precision counter was established by a cross comparison with a low-geometry counter—the two agreed to within 0.03%.

B. ABSOLUTE BETA COUNTING

Introduction to Beta Counting Techniques. If an experimenter is so unfortunate as to be faced with the problem of determining the disintegration rate of a beta emitter, his problem is much more complicated than the alpha assay problem already discussed. The complications arise from the effects of scattering and absorption of electrons in matter, combined with the distribution in energy of the beta particles. It is usual to combine all experimental quantities which affect the observed counting rate into a *counting yield* ϵ, which relates the observed counting rate R and the disintegration rate N_D:

$$\epsilon = R/N_D \qquad (50)$$

Although ϵ is usually determined experimentally, it can, in principle, be separated into the following factors (214): the geometry; the intrinsic efficiency of the detector; an absorption factor for the air between source and detector, in addition to the detector window; a correction for air scattering; a factor for the backscattering by the source support; a factor to correct for scattering by environment; and a correction for the self-absorption and self-scattering by the finite mass of the source. The review article by Steinberg (214) discusses the magnitudes and dependences of the various factors on the experimental situation.

It is usually possible to determine a beta disintegration rate with an end-window counter to better than 5%. The counting yield of an essentially weightless source on a thin backing can be standardized to this accuracy either by use of an absolute standard, or by use of experimentally determined values of geometry, absorption, and scattering effects.

Calibration standards must be used for assay of thick beta sources to an accuracy of better than 10%. A carrier-free sample of the desired activity is prepared and its disintegration rate determined. Aliquots of the sample are then processed, taking care that the amounts of carrier, mounting procedures, and other details are the same as for the unknown. In this way, the counting yield is measured directly for the particular experiment.

End-Window Counters. By far the most common detector in use at present is the end-window counter. Much of the early information on beta counting was obtained with end-window Geiger tubes, although they have now been largely supplanted by end-window proportional counters (Section

VI.4.B). The proportional counters are more stable and reliable, and because they usually are filled to one atmosphere pressure, their windows can be made very thin (0.2–1 mg./cm.^{2}) for good sensitivity to low-energy beta particles. The mechanical dimensions of end-window Geiger and proportional counters are similar, as are the dimensions of their source holders: therefore, some of the published data for Geiger counters can still be used in modern counting applications.

2π Counters. For counting either low-intensity samples, where a high geometry is needed, or low-energy beta particles, where it is desirable to eliminate the detector window, a 2π counter is very convenient. An additional advantage of this arrangement is that anisotropic scattering effects are less important here than in the end-window case.

The general procedure for calibration of the counting yield is similar to that described above for end-window counters. A carrier-free sample on a nearly weightless backing does not eliminate scattering in a 2π geometry, because some structural material is almost certain to be nearby: for this reason, it is advisable to standardize the counting yield for sources mounted on a backing which gives saturation backscattering.

4π Counting. The most generally used technique for primary standardization is the 4π geometry beta counter, or $4\pi\beta$ counter. This instrument was described briefly in Section VI.4.B. Coincident gamma rays or internal conversion electrons, when detected, are always counted simultaneously with the associated beta particle, and thus result only in a single count. Any discharges caused by scattering of the primary particle or by secondary radiation will also fall within the resolving time, and will not affect the measured rate.

A well-designed $4\pi\beta$ proportional counter will have a geometrical efficiency in excess of 99.5%, and a plateau whose slope is less than 0.1%; therefore, the accuracy with which the disintegration rate may be determined depends mainly on absorption in the source and in the mounting film. Absorption shall in all likelihood remain the factor which limits the accuracy of $4\pi\beta$ counting. Self-absorption was studied for specific source materials by Pate and Yaffe (170), and by Yaffe and Fishman (188), who showed how their correction method could be applied to other 4π counter sources.

The source–film absorption correction has been determined in three ways: (1) the "sandwich" procedure of Hawkings et al. (102), in which the counting rate of a source on a known thickness of backing is measured, followed by a determination with an identical film covering the sample; (2) a calculated correction, proposed by Seliger and co-workers (203), was based on measurements of 2π and 4π single-film and "sandwiched" counting rates; (3) a determination of the counting rate as a function of actual source film thickness was made by Smith (209), and has been studied exhaustively by Pate and Yaffe (171). Any of these methods is useful above a few hundred thousand electron volts, but (*3*), the absorption curve technique, appears to be the most accurate, even at energies below 100 keV.

Films to be used as source mounts should be rendered electrically conducting, preferably by vacuum evaporation of a metallic coating at least 2 μg./cm.² thick. This coating will guard against distortion of the electric field by electrostatic charging of the source film, or by penetration of the field of one counter into the other.

A systematic study of the general technique of $4\pi\beta$ counting has been published by Pate and Yaffe (169–172). Measurements at the National Bureau of Standards and the results of intercomparisons of sources by various laboratories are discussed by Seliger and co-workers (145, 203, 204). The proceedings of a symposium on the metrology of nuclides (188) contains a series of useful papers on the latest techniques of $4\pi\beta$ counting.

Some work has also been performed using liquid scintillation counters as 4π detectors. These techniques, which are as yet rather specialized and of limited application, are described in papers included in references 188 and 174.

Coincidence Counting.* When two radiations are emitted in sequence during the decay of a radionuclide, coincidence counting is a convenient and accurate method for determining the disintegration rate. Consider the simple case of a single beta group followed by a single gamma ray. The counting rate of the beta counter $\mathbf{R}_\beta$ is given by

$$\mathbf{R}_\beta = N_D \, \epsilon_\beta \tag{51}$$

where N_D is the disintegration rate and ϵ_β the counting yield. Similarly, the gamma-ray counting rate $\mathbf{R}_\gamma$ is

$$\mathbf{R}_\gamma = N_D \, \epsilon_\gamma \tag{52}$$

Here, ϵ_γ is the counting yield of the gamma detector. The coincidence rate N_C is

$$N_C = N_D \, \epsilon_\beta \, \epsilon_\gamma \tag{53}$$

which reduces to

$$N_D = \mathbf{R}_\beta \, \mathbf{R}_\gamma / N_C \tag{54}$$

Note that the determination of the disintegration rate by this technique does not require that the counting yields be known. The counting rates in the beta, gamma, and coincidence channels must be corrected for back-

* A recent report of the theory and practice of this technique was made by Campion (38).

ground rates and dead-time losses. Because each detector must only be sensitive to a single type of radiation, the background correction in the beta channel must also include the contribution arising from the gamma sensitivity.

An additional correction to the coincidence rate is the random coincidence rate, $N_r = 2\tau \, R_\beta \, R_\gamma$; the rates in the beta and gamma channels should be total rates before background subtraction. As previously, 2τ is the coincidence resolving time. Another coincidence "background" arises from the detection of gamma–gamma cascades in the two detectors, if the decay scheme is complex.

Nuclides with several beta groups may be assayed by the beta–gamma coincidence technique, if the sensitivity of either the beta or gamma detector is the same for all branches of the decay scheme (190). Because of its high, uniform efficiency, the $4\pi\beta$ counter makes a very useful beta detector for coincidence counting. When counting nuclides with complex decay schemes by the $4\pi\beta$–γ coincidence method, the corrections arising from the decay scheme usually turn out to be rather small (38).

Since the beta–gamma coincidence technique is insensitive to counting losses from absorption in the source and its backing, it offers another way of calibrating the counting yield for thick sources in a $4\pi\beta$ counter (38,94). With quantitative information about the decay scheme of a particular nuclide, it should be possible to standardize sources by $4\pi\beta$–γ coincidence counting to a few tenths of a per cent (38).

C. ABSOLUTE GAMMA COUNTING

Gamma-ray counting by the scintillation method was discussed in Section VI.1.C. Spectrometry at a defined solid angle will yield an accuracy of about 5%—more accurate data require calibration with sources of known disintegration rates. Integral counters, such as well-type scintillation detectors, must be standardized.

The most precise instrument for secondary standardization of gamma emitters is the high-pressure ionization chamber (Section VI.2.E). A precision of about 0.05% can be obtained when intercomparing sources. The coincidence method of absolute counting is not limited to beta–gamma counting, but may be extended to any coincident pair of radiations, such as beta–electron coincidences, x ray–gamma coincidences, and especially gamma–gamma coincidences. The National Bureau of Standards has used the gamma–gamma coincidence counting technique for assay of Co^{60} (174, 188). In this situation, where two cascade gamma rays are of equal intensities, disintegration rates can be obtained to as good an accuracy as by other methods.

VII. SOURCE MOUNTING

1. Introduction

By now it is probably obvious to the reader that the choice of a chemical separation procedure, the choice of a radiation detector, and the choice of source mount are not independent. Factors such as the nature of the radiation to be counted often will determine the type of source to be employed; the source, in turn, will usually place restrictions on the choice of chemical procedure (Section V) and counting equipment. There is so much variety in the interrelated factors which must be considered that this section will not attempt to set down firm rules for choosing the best source preparation method. Instead, some of the common techniques will be discussed in a general way so that the experimenter will be given sufficient information about methods in use to make a choice for his own problem.

For a more extensive discussion, it is suggested that the reader consult the summaries of the source preparation problem by Overman and Clark (176) and Slätis (207). These authors quote extensive references for further reading.

2. Desiccated Sources

A. EVAPORATION FROM SOLUTION

It is often desirable to prepare a source which is very thin. The most straightforward approach to this problem is evaporation of an aliquot of a carrier-free solution on a suitable backing. To produce a thin source by this technique is very difficult, because it is essential that the solution shall contain no chemical compounds which will contribute appreciable mass to the final deposit. A technique which avoids concentrating impurities in the final product is the use of a very small bed of ion-exchange resin, to which the carrier-free activity is adsorbed; after washing, the activity is eluted in the smallest possible volume of reagent (99).

An unavoidable feature of evaporation from solution is that any solids present will not form a uniform deposit. In some experiments, such as $4\pi\beta$ counting of low-energy beta particles, self-absorption of aggregates may be excessive, and another method of depositing the source may be required.

Metal Backing Plates. Alpha particles exhibit a short range in matter, and sources of these particles must be quite thin. As was seen in Section VI.7.A, alpha backscattering is small and is easily determined, so a metal plate makes a convenient source backing.

If the volume of solution to be evaporated on a metal plate is very large, it may be helpful to confine the solution to the desired region by a border of Zapon lacquer. After drying, the lacquer and any volatile impurities can be removed by ignition in an induction heater or an open flame, provided that the sample proper is nonvolatile. Further information on the use of metal foils as source backings will be found in reviews by Dodson *et al.* (60) and by Hufford and Scott (110).

A very useful spreading technique (60) for preparation of uniform foils of heavy elements calls for mixing the nitrate of the desired element, dissolved in an organic solvent, with a dilute solution of Zapon lacquer. This mixture is painted on a metal plate, and, after drying, the plate is heated to destroy the organic residue and to convert the nitrate to the oxide. After each ignition the deposit is rubbed with tissue to insure that successive layers will adhere. Quite uniform deposits with smooth vitreous surfaces can be prepared by application of many successive coats, each very thin. This technique is generally useful for any case where the element deposited has a nonvolatile compound which can be dissolved in an organic solvent; the foil must have a melting point high enough to withstand ignition.

Another technique which makes use of an organic solution of a nitrate has been described by Carswell and Milsted (40). In their method the solution is sprayed from a capillary tube by the influence of a strong electric field. The space from the capillary tip to the metal plate is adjusted so that only fine, dry particles are collected. Thin, uniform sources may be prepared, even on extremely thin gold-coated plastic films (75).

Very Thin Backings. In many beta counting applications, it is necessary to mount carrier-free sources on as thin a backing as possible. The usual technique is to transfer an aliquot of the appropriate solution onto the thin film by means of a micro pipette. The liquid is carefully evaporated by gently heating with an infrared lamp; the process is accelerated by flowing a stream of air over the source during evaporation.

The methods for preparing the thin films have been exhaustively reviewed in a monograph by Yaffe (240). The article on source and window technique by Slätis (207) remains a very useful reference on thin films and other aspects of the source problem.

Gamma-Ray Sources. Although any of the techniques already described can be used to prepare gamma-ray sources, the relatively low absorption of gamma rays by matter makes possible a rather simple and rapid technique for mounting an aliquot of solution for gamma-ray assay. This method uses a small disk of blotting paper or a chemist's "filter accelerator" taped onto a card. An aliquot of the solution to be determined is merely allowed to soak into the paper. After the sample has been dried by using an infrared heat lamp, the source should be covered by cellophane or Mylar tape.

B. USE OF SLURRIES

Frequently, it is convenient to transfer small amounts of precipitate to a source mount and evaporate the solvent. The precipitate may, for example, lie collected in the tip of a centrifuge tube at the last step of a chemical separation procedure. A suitable organic liquid (e.g., alcohol or acetone) is added, and the resulting slurry is drawn into a transfer pipette; when discharging the contents of the pipette into a planchet, care must be exercised to insure that the spreading of the precipitate is uniform. After drawing off excess liquid, the sample is dried on the planchet, and then covered with a thin plastic film to prevent spillage.

There are occasions in which it may prove convenient to perform the final centrifugation in a demountable centrifuge tube whose bottom is a source planchet. This method has the advantage that the final deposits obtained are more uniform than those formed by pipetting slurries.

C. FILTRATION OF PRECIPITATES

When large numbers of samples must be prepared, the most convenient method is filtration, using a filter paper disk as a combination source mount and filter. Rather large masses of precipitate can be accommodated, and with proper technique the area and thickness can be controlled sufficiently to insure good reliability.

Several designs for filtration devices have been published (167), and a few are available commercially. In all of these a disk of fine grade filter paper (e.g., Whatman No. 42) lies on a flat support, which may be either a sintered glass filter disk or perforated stainless steel plate, attached to the end of a tube. A hollow cylinder of glass or stainless steel, into which the slurry is introduced, is clamped firmly over the top of the filter paper disk. Once the precipitate is caught on the filter paper, it may be washed and dried before removing it from the apparatus. If there is a tendency for the cake of precipitate to break up, a dilute solution of organic binder such as collodion may be passed through the filter before the final drying.

When the weight of final precipitate is needed to determine a chemical yield, a tare weight should be determined by using several filter paper disks identical to those employed for the unknown. Naturally, the tare papers should be subjected to the same wash solutions, binder, and drying procedure as the unknown.

3. Sublimation

Some of the most uniform sources are prepared by sublimation in vacuum. This method is applicable when the radionuclide of interest can be prepared in a chemical compound whose vapor pressure is at least 0.1 mm. Hg at a temperature below that for rapid decomposition. Examples of this technique will be found in references 60, 110, and 3.

The apparatus consists of a demountable vacuum chamber, in which is situated either a crucible or a ribbon filament, with the collector plate a fraction of an inch away. Usually it is desirable to evaporate the source solution onto a shallow trough or depression in the filament, so when the filament is heated the sublimed material is collimated onto the collecting plate. A crucible, heated with electrical resistance wire or by electron bombardment, has similar collimating properties.

For the preparation of thin sources, it is helpful to be able to swing the collector away during the initial heating of the sample. It is then possible to "cook off" various impurities (such as organic residues) at low temperature, without subliming them onto the source mount.

Most of the procedures for vacuum sublimation are time consuming and have yields of less than 50%. Pate and Yaffe (170) have designed a system for subliming from a crucible onto a thin film with nearly 100% yield. Their results suggest that it should be possible to prepare sources which are not only uniform and thin, but also contain a known aliquot of a stock solution. The possibilities of such a technique in the fields of $4\pi\beta$ and alpha-particle counting are very promising.

4. Electrodeposition

Perhaps the most convenient source mounting technique, except for simple evaporation of a solution, is electrodeposition. Although it is not, in principle, as generally applicable as vacuum evaporation, it has enjoyed widespread use, especially for samples of the heavy-element alpha-particle emitters. Very uniform films can be obtained by this method, ranging from trace amounts to a few mg./cm.^{2}.

Because the method is so well suited to the preparation of alpha-particle sources, extensive literature has been published on the electrodeposition of the heavy elements. Procedures for polonium, thorium, uranium, neptunium, and plutonium have been reported in the published records of the Manhattan Project (41,60,110) and an article by Ko (127) gives electrodeposition procedures for all the actinide elements through curium. Where no procedures are available for carrier-free electrodeposition of a particular element, information in the standard analytical and electrochemical texts may be used as a guide; however, as was pointed out in Section V.2.D., the carrier-free element may not behave in the same way as do weighable amounts. In such a situation, it may be helpful to add a small amount of carrier to avoid these difficulties.

The apparatus for electrodepositing radionuclides on counting plates has been described in the literature (e.g., 41, 60, 110, 167). Several devices are available commercially.

5. Sources Containing Gases

Samples of certain nuclides, notably the rare gases, are most conveniently assayed as gases. The experimenter may elect to introduce the gas into an ionization chamber, proportional counter, or Geiger counter as a component of the detector gas; or, he may choose to contain the gas in some way and mount it externally to the counter.

The highly specialized and well-developed techniques for internal gas counting have been adequately described in the current literature, as the list of references given by Overman and Clark (167) attests. Application of the method to the use of nuclides such as C^{14} (as CO_2) has been treated by Tolbert and Siri (221).

A gas simply may be pumped into a container having a thin window for the exit of the particles to be counted. In spite of its convenience, this technique is not often used for absolute counting because the counting geometry of such a diffuse source is not well defined. If gamma-ray counting is to be performed, a gas sample may be contained by adsorption on a bed of activated charcoal, or on one of the clathrates. The trap requires such thick construction material that beta counting is usually rather inefficient, and gamma-ray counting is to be preferred.

A method for preparing thin, permanent samples of rare gases on metals has been described by Momyer and Hyde (151). In their method the rare gas is introduced, along with nitrogen or air as carrier gas, into a glass chamber containing two electrodes, which may be either two parallel platinum plates or a helical anode surrounding a central wire collector (cathode) of platinum. A glow discharge is struck between the two electrodes at a pressure of 100–1000 microns, taking care to limit the current to only 2–3 ma. In 5 min. it is possible to obtain yields of a few per cent. No detectable loss of gas occurs from these sources at room temperature, and they appear to be quite thin.

6. Liquid Sources

For the beta counting of liquid samples, the liquid scintillation method (Section VI.1.B) is ideal. The current literature may be consulted for the latest recipes for samples compatible with the most common solution scintillators. General information on the subject may be found in references 221, 167, and 7.

Gamma-ray emitters may be contained very conveniently in small, biological-type test tubes, for counting in a well-type NaI(Tl) scintillation counter (Section VI.1.C). Larger aliquots of solution may be contained in centrifuge tubes of up to 50-ml. capacity; these may be assayed in high-pressure, gamma-sensitive ionization chambers, such as were described in Section VI.2.E.

VIII. OTHER AREAS OF RESEARCH INVOLVING RADIOACTIVITY

Mapping the course of a rapidly expanding scientific field is no easier than covering fully its present status, as our foregoing treatment aptly illustrates. Exigencies of space permitted only brief comments on applications to such huge areas of interest as analytical chemistry and chemical kinetics. Certainly, increased availability of tracers as well as improved (and less expensive) counting equipment will greatly expand these areas of radionuclide use. We did not deal directly with the important related subject of nuclear reactor chemistry. This specialty, which includes the chemical behavior of the materials used in reactors as well as the chemical reprocessing of nuclear fuel, will grow in importance with the "coming of age" of the nuclear power industry. Other industrial uses, e.g., beta-ray gaging or thickness measuring, were deemed beyond the scope of this volume.

We have discussed nuclear chemistry, that hybrid discipline which bridges chemistry and nuclear physics. Nuclear chemists have contributed mightily to the present knowledge of radioactive decay, nuclear reactions, and fission of nuclei, as well as to the state of the art of radiation detection. No doubt their efforts will be stimulated by the construction of new accelerators and nuclear reactors as well as the continued slackening of physicists' interest in fields involving low energies or complex nuclei.

The earliest nuclear chemists, specifically Mme. Curie and her colleagues, recognized the possibility of dating minerals and meteorites by making use of the long-lived radioactive nuclides. From its faltering pre-World War II status, this field of nuclear geochemistry has grown tremendously. The current upsurge in space activities is causing an even more rapid quickening of interest. In fact, there has recently been established a Gordon Research Conference on the Chemistry and Physics of Space.

References

Many of the references below are to documents available from the Office of Technical Services (OTS), Department of Commerce, Washington 25, D. C., and the Superintendent of Documents (Supt. Doc.), U. S. Government Printing Office, Washington 25, D. C. In each case the price of the document is given.

1. Ajzenberg-Selove, F., Ed., *Nuclear Spectroscopy*, Vols. I and II Academic Press, New York, 1960.
2. Arnold, J. R., "Low Level Counting 1" in *Measurements and Standards of Radioactivity, Proceedings of an Informal Conference*, Easton, Md., October 9–11, 1957, Pub. No. 573, National Academy of Sciences–National Research Council, Washington, D. C., 1958, p. 110.

3. Asaro, F., F. L. Reynolds, and I. Perlman, *Phys. Rev.*, **87**, 277 (1952).
4. Bardeen, J., "Flow of Electrons and Holes in Semiconductors," in E. U. Condon and H. Odishaw, Eds., *Handbook of Physics*, McGraw-Hill, 1958, Part 8, Chapter 4.
5. (a) Bayhurst, B. P., and R. J. Prestwood, *J. Inorg. Nucl. Chem.*, *23*, 173 (1961). (b) R. J. Prestwood and B. P. Bayhurst, *Phys. Rev.*, **121**, 1438 (1961). (c) B. P. Bayhurst and R. J. Prestwood, LA-2493 (OTS—$1.25).
6. (a) Beck, C. K., Ed., *Nuclear Reactors for Research*, Van Nostrand, Princeton, 1957. (b) *Research Reactors*, U. S. Atomic Energy Commission, McGraw-Hill, New York, 1955. (c) *Proceedings of the International Conference on the Peaceful Uses of Atomic Energy* (Geneva, Aug. 8–20, 1955) Vol. 2, United Nations, New York, 1956, p. 233. (d) *Proceedings of the International Conference on the Peaceful Uses of Atomic Energy* (Geneva, Sept. 1–13, 1958) Vol. 10, United Nations, Geneva, 1958. (e) *Directory of Nuclear Reactors, Vol. I; Power Reactors; Vol. II and III Research, Test, and Experimental Reactors*, International Atomic Energy Agency, Vienna, 1958, 1959, and 1960.
7. Bell, C. G., and F. N. Hayes, Eds., *Conference on Liquid Scintillation Counting*, Pergamon Press, New York, 1958.
8. Bell, P. R., "The Scintillation Method" in K. Siegbahn, Ed., *Beta- and Gamma-Ray Spectroscopy*, North Holland Publishing Company, Amsterdam, 1955, p. 132.
9. Bell, P. R., J. Jauch, and J. M. Cassidy, *Science*, **115**, 12 (1952).
10. Bell, R. E., "Measurement by Delayed Coincidences," in K. Siegbahn, Ed., *Beta- and Gamma-Ray Spectroscopy*, North Holland Publishing Company, Amsterdam, 1955, p. 494.
11. Bethe, H. A., *Ann. Physik*, **5**, 325 (1930).
12. Bethe, H. A., *Revs. Modern Phys.*, **22**, 213 (1950).
13. Bethe, H. A., and J. Ashkin, "Passage of Radiations Through Matter," in E. Segré, Ed., *Experimental Nuclear Physics*, Vol. I, Wiley, New York, 1953, Part II.
14. Bethe, H. A., and W. Heitler, *Proc. Roy. Soc. (London)*, **A146**, 83 (1934).
15. Biegeleisen, J. A., *Ann. Rev. Nucl. Sci.*, **2**, 221 (1952).
16. Biondi, F. J., Ed., *Transistor Technology*, Vols. 2 and 3, Van Nostrand, Princeton, N. J., 1958.
17. Birkhoff, R. D., *Health Physics Division Annual Progress Report for Period Ending July 31, 1959*, Oak Ridge National Laboratory Report ORNL-2806, 1959, p. 153 (OTS—$3.50).
18. Birks, J. B., *IRE Trans. Nucl. Sci.*, *NS-7*, Nos. 2–3, 2 (1960).
19. Blankenship, J. L., and C. J. Borkowski, *IRE Trans. on Nucl. Sci.*, **NS-7**, Nos. 2–3, 190 (1960); *ibid.*, **NS-8**, No. 1, 17 (1961).
20. Blatt, J. M., and V. F. Weisskopf, *Theoretical Nuclear Physics*, Wiley, New York, 1952.
21. (a) Bohr, A., in *Proceedings of the International Conference on the Peaceful Uses of Atomic Energy* (Geneva, Aug. 8–20, 1955), Vol. II, United Nations, New York, 1956, p. 151. (b) P. Fong, *Phys. Rev.*, **102**, 434 (1956).
22. (a) Bohr, N., and J. A. Wheeler, *Phys. Rev.*, **56**, 426 (1939). (b) J. Frankel, *Phys. Rev.*, **55**, 987 (1939); *J. Phys. USSR*, **1**, 125 (1939). (c) W. J. Swiatecki, Swiatecki, W. J., "Deformation Energy of a Charged Drop. III. Further Developments" in *Proceedings of the Second International Conference on the Peaceful Uses of Atomic Energy*, Geneva, 1958. Vol. XV, United Nations, Geneva, 1958, p. 248.
23. Bohr, N., *Phil. Mag.*, **25**, Series 6, p. 10 (1913); *Kgl. Danske Videnskab. Selskab. Mat-fys. Medd.*, **18**, No. 8 (1948).

24. Bothe, W., "Passage of Electrons Through Matter," in Geiger, H., and K. Scheele Eds., *Handbuch der Physik-Encyclopedia of Physics*, Vol. XXII, Part 2, 2nd ed. Springer, Berlin, 1933.

25. (a) Boyd, G. E., *Ann. Rev. Phys. Chem.*, **2**, 309 (1951). (b) O. Samuelson, *Ion Exchangers in Analytical Chemistry*, Wiley, New York, 1953. (c) H. Walton *Ann. Rev. Phys. Chem.*, **10**, 123 (1959).

26. Bradt, H., et al., *Helv. Phys. Acta*, **19**, 222 (1946).

27. (a) Bretscher, E., and D. J. Hughes, Eds., *Physics of Nuclear Fission*, Pergamon, New York, 1958. (b) Hanna et al., Eds., *Proceedings of the Symposium on the Physics of Fission* (Chalk River, Ontario, May 14–18, 1958) Atomic Energy of Canada Report CRP-642A (Atomic Energy of Canada—$5.28). (c) E. Hyde, *A Review of Nuclear Fission, Parts I and II*, University of California Radiation Laboratory Reports UCRL-9065 and UCRL-9036. (d) A. Kraut, *Nucleonik*, **2**, 105, 149 (1960). (e) *Proceedings of the International Conference on the Peaceful Uses of Atomic Energy* (Geneva, Aug. 8–20, 1955), Vol. II, United Nations, New York, 1956, pp. 151–233; ibid., Vol. VII, pp. 3–26. (f) *Proceedings of the second International Conference on the Peaceful Uses of Atomic Energy* (Geneva, Sept. 1–13, 1957), Vol. XV, United Nations, Geneva, 1958, pp. 149–475. (g) R. W. Spence and G. P. Ford, *Ann. Rev. Nucl. Sci.*, **2**, 399 (1953). (h) J. A. Wheeler, *Physica*, **22**, 1103 (1956).

28. Briggs, G. H., *Proc. Roy. Soc. (London)*, **A114**, 341 (1927).

29. Bromley, D. A., and E. W. Vogt, Eds., *Proceedings of the International Conference on Nuclear Structure* (Kingston, Canada, Aug. 29–Sept. 3, 1960), University of Toronto Press, Toronto, Canada and North Holland Publishing Company, Amsterdam, 1960.

30. Brown, R. E., and N. Jarmie, *Index and Annotated Bibliography of Range and Stopping Cross Section Data*, Los Alamos National Laboratory Report LA-2156, 1958 (OTS—$2.00).

31. Brown, W. L., *IRE, Trans. Nucl. Sci.*, NS-8, No. 1, 2 (1960); "Properties of Space Charge Regions," in J. W. T. Dabbs and F. J. Walter, Eds., *Semiconductor Nuclear Particle Detectors*, Publication No. 871, National Academy of Sciences—National Research Council, Washington, 1961.

32. Buck, W. L., *IRE, Trans. Nucl. Sci.*, NS-7, Nos. 2 and 3, 11 (1960).

33. Burhop, E. H. S., *The Auger Effect*, Cambridge University Press, Cambridge, 1952.

34. Burrill, E. A., and M. H. MacGregor, *Nucleonics*, **18**, No. 12, 64 (1960).

35. Caldwell, D. O., and J. R. Armstrong, *Rev. Sci. Instr.*, **23**, 508 (1952).

36. Cameron, A. G. W., *A Revised Semi-Empirical Atomic Mass Formula*, Atomic Energy of Canada Report CRP-690.

37. Campbell, E. C., and F. Nelson, *J. Inorg. Nucl. Chem.*, **3**, 233 (1956).

38. Campion, P. J., *Intern. J. Appl. Radiation Isotopes*, **4**, 232 (1959).

39. Carlson, T. A., and W. S. Koski, *J. Chem. Phys.*, **23**, 1596 (1955).

40. Carswell, D. J., and J. Milsted, *J. Nucl. Energy*, **4**, 51 (1957).

41. Casto, C. C., in C. J. Rodden, N. R. Furman, E. H. Huffman, L. L. Quill, T. D. Price, and J. I. Watters, Eds., *Analytical Chemistry of the Manhattan Project*, National Nuclear Energy Series, Div. VIII-1, McGraw-Hill, New York, 1950, Chapter 23.

42. Čerenkov, P. A., *Compt. rend. Acad. Sci. U.S.S.R.*, **8**, 451 (1934).

43. Chase, R. L., *Rev. Sci. Instr.*, **31**, 945 (1960).

44. Chase, R. L., *Nuclear Pulse Spectrometry*, McGraw-Hill, New York, 1961.

45. Chetham-Strode, A., J. R. Tarrant, and R. J. Silva, *IRE, Trans. on Nucl. Sci.*, NS-8, No. 1, 59 (1961).

46. Choppin, Gregory R., *Experimental Nuclear Chemistry*, Prentice-Hall, Englewood Cliffs, N. J., 1961.
47. Coleman, R. F., B. E. Hawker, L. P. O'Connor, and J. L. Perkin, *Proc. Phys. Soc. (London)*, **73**, 215 (1959).
48. Corson, D. R., and R. R. Wilson, *Rev. Sci. Instr.*, **19**, 207 (1948); R. R. Wilson, D. R. Corson, and C. P. Baker, *Particle and Quantum Detectors*, Preliminary Report No. 7, National Research Council, Washington, D. C., January, 1950.
49. Coryell, C. D. and N. Sugarman, Eds., *Radiochemical Studies: The Fission Products*, National Nuclear Energy Series, Div. IV, Vol. IX, McGraw-Hill, New York, 1951.
50. Craig, L. C., *Anal. Chem.*, **22**, 1346 (1950).
51. Crouthamel, C. E., Ed., *Applied Gamma-Ray Spectrometry*, Pergamon Press, New York, 1960.
52. Curran, S. C., "The Proportional Counter as Detector and Spectrometer," in S. Flügge and E. Creutz, Eds., *Handbuch der Physik–Encyclopedia of Physics*, Springer, Berlin, 1958.
53. Curran, S. C., "Proportional Counter Spectrometry," in K. Siegbahn, Ed., *Beta- and Gamma-Ray Spectroscopy*, North Holland Publishing Co., Amsterdam, 1955, Vol. XLV Chapter VI.
54. Curtis, M. L., J. W. Heyd, R. G. Olt and J. F. Eichelberger, *Nucleonics*, **13** (5), 38 (1955).
55. Davisson, C. M., "Interactions of Gamma Radiation with Matter," in K. Siegbahn, Ed., *Beta- and Gamma-Ray Spectroscopy*, North Holland Publishing Co., Amsterdam, 1955.
56. De Benedetti, S., and R. W. Findley, "The Coincidence Method," in S. Flügge and E. Creutz, Eds., *Handbuch der Physik–Encyclopedia of Physics*, Vol. XLV, Springer, Berlin, 1958, p. 222.
57. Delahay, P. *New Instrumental Methods in Electrochemistry*, Interscience, New York, 1954.
58. (a) DeVoe, J. R., C. K. Kim, and W. W. Meinke, *Talanta*, **3**, 298 (1960). (b) Ruch, R. R., J. R. DeVoe, and W. W. Meinke, *Talanta*, **9**, 33 (1962). (c) DeVoe, J. R., H. W. Nass, and W. W. Meinke, *Anal. Chem.*, **33**, 1713 (1961).
59. DeVoe, J. R., *Radioactive Contamination of Materials Used in Scientific Research*, Publication 895, National Academy of Sciences–National Research Council, Washington, D. C., 1961.
60. Dodson, R. W., A. C. Graves, L. Helmholz, D. L. Hufford, R. M. Potter, and J. G. Povelites, in A. C. Graves and D. K. Froman, Eds., *Miscellaneous Physical and Chemical Techniques of the Los Alamos Project*, National Nuclear Energy Series, Div. 5, Vol. 3, McGraw-Hill, New York, 1951, Chapter 1.
61. Donovan, P. F., "Paint-on Particle Detectors," in J. W. T. Dabbs and F. J. Walter, Eds., *Semiconductor Nuclear Particle Detectors*, Publication 871, National Academy of Sciences–National Research Council, Washington, 1961.
62. Elliott, J. H., *Thick Radiation Detectors Made by Ion Drift*, University of California Radiation Laboratory Report UCRL-9538, 1961.
63. Elmore, W. C., and M. Sands, *Electronics*, McGraw-Hill, New York, 1949.
64. Emmer, T. L., *IRE Trans. on Nucl. Sci.*, **NS-8**, No. 1, 140 (1961).
65. Evans, R. D., *The Atomic Nucleus*, McGraw-Hill, New York, 1955.
66. Fairstein, E., "Electrometers and Amplifiers," in A. H. Snell, Ed., *Nuclear Instrumentation and Methods*, Wiley, New York, 1961.
67. Fairstein, E., *Rev. Sci. Instr.*, **27**, 475 (1956).

68. Fairstein, E., *IRE, Trans. Nucl. Sci.*, **NS-8**, No. 1, 129 (1961).
69. Fairstein, E., in *Instrumentation and Controls Division Annual Progress Report for Period Ending July 1, 1957*, Oak Ridge National Laboratory Report ORNL-2480, 1957, pp. 1–3 (OTS—$6.30, microfilm).
70. Fano, U., *Nucleonics*, **11** (8), 8 (1953).
71. Feather, N., *Proc. Cambridge Phil. Soc.*, **34**, 599 (1938).
72. *Federal Register*, **22**, 449 (1957).
73. Finston, H., and J. Miskel, *Ann. Rev. Nucl. Sci.*, **5**, 269 (1955).
74. Flügge, S., and E. Creutz, Eds., *Handbuch der Physik–Encyclopedia of Physics*, Vol. XLV, Springer, Berlin, 1958.
75. Fraser, J. S., and J. C. D. Milton, *Physics Division Progress Report—January 1, 1958 to March 31, 1958*, Atomic Energy of Canada Report AECL-587, 1958, p. 14 (Atomic Energy of Canada, Ltd.—$1.50).
76. Freedman, M. S., T. B. Novey, F. T. Porter, and F. Wagner, Jr., *Rev. Sci. Instr.*, **27**, 716 (1956).
77. Freiser, H., and G. H. Morrison, *Ann. Rev. Nucl. Sci.*, **9**, 221 (1959).
78. Friedlander, G., and J. W. Kennedy, *Nuclear and Radiochemistry*, Wiley, New York, 1955.
79. Friedman, A., private communication.
80. Fulbright, H. W., "Ionization Chambers in Nuclear Physics," in S. Flügge and E. Creutz, Eds., *Handbuch der Physik–Encyclopedia of Physics*, Vol. XLV, Springer, Berlin, 1958.
81. Gardner, D. G., *Nucl. Phys.*, **29**, 373 (1961).
82. Gardner, D. G. and J. Kantele, *Nucl. Phys.*, **35**, 363 (1962).
83. Gardner, D. G., and W. W. Meinke, *Int. J. Appl. Radiation Isotopes*, **3**, 232 (1958).
84. *General Electric Chart of the Nuclides* (obtainable from Knolls Atomic Power Laboratory); *Trilinear Chart of Nuclear Species*, H. Sullivan (Supt. Doc.—$2.00).
85. Ghiorso, A., T. Sikkeland, A. E. Larsh, and R. M. Latimer, *Phys. Rev. Letters*, **6**, 473 (1961).
86. Gillespie, A., *Signal, Noise, and Resolution in Nuclear Counter Amplifiers*, McGraw-Hill, New York, 1953.
87. Reference 86, p. 69.
88. Glendenin, L. E., R. P. Metcalf, T. B. Novey, and C. D. Coryell, in C. D. Coryell and N. Sugarman, Eds., *Radiochemical Studies: The Fission Products*, National Nuclear Energy Series, Div. IV, Vol. IX, McGraw-Hill, 1951, Book III, p. 1629.
89. Glover, K. M., and G. R. Hall, *Nature*, **173**, 991 (1954).
90. Goulding, F. S., R. W. Nicholson, J. B. Waugh, *Nucl. Instr. Methods*, **8**, 272 (1960).
91. Goulding, F. S., and R. A. McNaught, *Nucl. Instr. Methods*, **8**, 282 (1960).
92. Green, A. E. S., *Nuclear Physics*, McGraw-Hill, New York, 1955.
93. Gruverman, I. J., and P. Kruger, *Intern. J. Appl. Radiation Isotopes*, **5**, 21 (1959).
94. Gunnink, R., L. J. Colby, Jr., and J. W. Cobble, *Anal. Chem.*, **31**, 796 (1959).
95. Hahn, O., *Applied Radiochemistry*, Cornell University, Ithaca, 1936.
    Bonner, N. A., and M. Kahn, in A. C. Wahl and N. A. Bonner, Eds., *Radioactivity Applied to Chemistry*, Wiley, New York, 1951, Chap. VI.
96. Halliday, D., *Introductory Nuclear Physics*, 2nd ed., Wiley, New York, 1955.
97. Hanna, G. C., "Alpha-Radioactivity," in E. Segrè, Ed., *Experimental Nuclear Physics*, Vol. III, Wiley, New York, 1959, p. 54.
98. Hanna, G. C., reference 97, p. 192 ff.

99. Hansen, P. G., and R. K. Sheline, *Nucl. Instr.*, **2**, 39 (1958); S. Bjornholm, O. B Nielsen, R. K. Sheline, *Nature*, **178**, 1110 (1956).
100. Harbottle, G., *J. Am. Chem. Soc.*, **82**, 805 (1960).
101. Harvey, B. G., *Ann. Rev. Nucl. Sci.*, **10**, 235 (1960).
102. Hawkings, R. C., W. F. Merritt, and J. H. Craven, *Proceedings of Symposium on Maintenance of Standards, National Physical Laboratory, 1951,* H. M. Stationers Office, London, 1952.
103. Hayes, F. N., D. G. Ott, and V. N. Kerr, *Nucleonics*, **14**, No. 1, 42 (1956).
104. Heath, R. L., *Scintillation Spectrometry Gamma-Ray Spectrum Catalogue,* Phillips Petroleum Company, Atomic Energy Division Report IDO-16408, 1957 (OTS—$4.75).
105. Heitler, W., *The Quantum Theory of Radiation,* Oxford University Press, London, 2d ed., 1944.
106. Henderson, G. H., *Proc. Roy. Soc. (London)*, **A102**, 496 (1922); **A109**, 157 (1925).
107. Henisch, H. K., *Rectifying Semiconductor Contracts,* Clarendon Press, Oxford, 1957.
108. Howard, F. T., *Cyclotrons and High-Energy Accelerators—1958,* Oak Ridge National Laboratory Report ORNL-2644, 1959 (OTS—$5.00).
109. Hoyaux, M., and I. Dujardin, *Nucleonics*, **4**, No. 6, 12 (1946). Thonemann, P. C., *Progr. Nucl. Phys.*, **3**, 219 (1953).
110. Hufford, D. L., and B. F. Scott, in G. T. Seaborg, J. J. Katz, and W. M. Manning, Eds., *The Transuranium Elements,* National Nuclear Energy Series, Div. IV, Vol. XIV-B, McGraw-Hill, New York, 1949, p. 1149.
111. Hughes, D. J., *Pile Neutron Research,* Addison-Wesley, Cambridge, Mass., 1953.
112. Hughes, D. J., and R. B. Schwartz, *Neutron Cross Sections,* Brookhaven National Laboratory Report BNL-325, 1958 (Supt. Doc.—$4.50). Hughes, D. J., B. A. Magurno, and M. K. Brussel, *Neutron Cross Section,* Supplement No. 1 to BNL-325, 1960 (Supt. Doc.—$2.00).
113. Jarmie, N., and J. D. Seagrave, Eds., *Charged Particle Cross Sections (Hydrogen to Fluorine),* Los Alamos Scientific Laboratory Report LA-2014, 1957 (OTS—$10.20, microfilm). Smith, D. B., N. Jarmie, and J. D. Seagrove, Eds., *Charged Particle Cross Sections, Neon to Chromium,* Los Alamos Scientific Laboratory Report LA-2424 (OTS—$2.50).
114. Johnson, N. R., E. Eichler, G. D. O'Kelley, J. W. Chase, and J. T. Wasson, *Phys. Rev.*, **122**, 1546 (1961).
115. Jones, H. B., *Proc. Health Phys. Soc.,* Univ. of Michigan (June 25–27, 1957).
116. Jonscher, A. K., *Principles of Semiconductor Device Operation,* G. Bell and Sons, London, 1960.
117. Jordan, W. H., *Ann. Rev. Nucl. Sci.*, **1**, 207 (1952).
118. Kallmann, H., and M. Furst, in C. G. Bell and F. N. Hayes, Eds., *Conference on Liquid Scintillation Counting,* Northwestern Univ., 1957, Pergamon Press, New York, 1958, p. 3.
119. Kapitza, P., *Proc. Roy. Soc. (London)*, **A106**, 602 (1924).
120. Katcoff, S., *Nucleonics*, **18**, No. 11, 201 (1960).
121. Katz, L., and A. S. Penfold, *Revs. Mod. Phys.*, **24**, 28 (1952).
122. Kelley, G. G., *I.R.E. National Conventional Record,* Part 9, p. 63 (1957).
123. Ketelle, B. H., *Phys. Rev.*, **80**, 758 (1950).
124. Ketelle, B. H., and A. R. Brosi, Oak Ridge National Laboratory, Oak Ridge, Tennessee, private communication.
125. Kingston, R. H., Ed., *Conference on the Physics of Semiconductor Surfaces,* Phila., 1956, University of Pennsylvania Press, Philadelphia, 1957.

126. Klein, O., and Y. Nishina, *Z. Physik.* **52**, 853 (1929).

127. Ko, R., *Nucleonics*, **15** (1) 72 (1957).

128. Koch, H. W., and R. W. Johnston, Eds., *Multichannel Pulse Height Analyzers*, Publication 467, National Academy of Sciences–National Research Council, Washington, 1957.

129. Koch, H. W., reference 128, pp. 19–31.

130. Koch, J., and K. O. Nielsen, "An Electromagnetic Isotope Separator and Its Application in Laboratories for Nuclear Research" in *Proceedings of the International Conference on the Peaceful Uses of Atomic Energy*, Geneva, 1955. Vol. XIV, United Nations, New York, 1956, p. 39.

131. Kohman, T. P., in G. T. Seaborg, Ed., *The Transuranium Elements*, National Nuclear Energy Series, Div. IV, Vol. XIV-B, Part II, McGraw-Hill, 1950.

132. Korff, S. A., *Electron and Nuclear Counters*, Van Nostrand, New York, 1955, 2d ed.

133. Korff, A. A., "Geiger Counters," in S. Flügge and E. Creutz, Eds., *Handbuch der Physik—Encyclopedia of Physics*, Vol. XLV Springer, Berlin, 1958, p. 52.

134. Kraus, K. A., and F. Nelson, *Ann. Rev. Nucl. Sci.*, **7**, 31 (1957); "Anion Exchange Studies of the Fission Products" in *Proceedings of the International Conference on the Peaceful Uses of Atomic Energy*, Geneva, 1955 Vol. 7, United Nations, New York, 1956, p. 113.

135. Kulp, J. L., "Low Level Counting 2." in *Measurements and Standards of Radioactivity, Proceedings of an Informal Conference*, Easton, Md., October 9–11, 1957. (Nuclear Science Series Report No. 24, NRC Pub. No. 573), National Academy of Sciences–National Research Council, Washington, D. C., 1958, p. 121.

136. Lazar, N. H., R. C. Davis, and P. R. Bell, *I.R.E. Trans. Nucl. Sci.*, **NS-3**, No. 4, 136 (1956); *Nucleonics*, **14**, (4), 52 (1956).

137. Lazar, N. H., and E. D. Klema, *Phys. Rev.*, **98**, 710 (1955).

138. Lee, T. D., and C. N. Yang, *Phys. Rev.*, **104**, 254 (1956).

139. Lewis, I. A. D., and F. H. Wells, *Millimicrosecond Pulse Techniques*, 2nd revised ed., Pergamon Press, New York, 1959, p. 302.

140. Livingood, J. J., *Principles of Cyclic Particle Accelerators*, Van Nostrand, Princeton, 1961.

141. Love, D. L., *Anal. Chim. Acta.*, **18**, 72 (1958).

142. Love, D. L., and A. E. Greendale, *Anal. Chem.*, **32**, 780 (1960).

143. *Low-Noise Amplifiers for Use with Solid-State Detectors*, Office of Technical Information Extension, U. S. Atomic Energy Commission, Report TID-6119, August, 1960 (OTS—$0.50).

144. Lyon, W. S., and S. A. Reynolds, *Nucleonics*, **14** (12) 44 (1956).

145. Mann, W. B., and H. H. Seliger, *Preparation, Maintenance, and Application of Standards of Radioactivity*, National Bureau of Standards Circular 594, 1958.

146. Martin, J. A., and F. L. Green, *Nucl. Sci. Eng.*, **1**, 185 (1956); **7**, 387 (1960).

147. Martin, J. A., R. S. Livingston, R. L. Murray, and M. Rankin, *Nucleonics*, **13** (3), p. 28 (1955).

148. McMillan, E. M., "Particle Accelerators" in E. Segré, Ed., *Experimental Nuclear Physics*, Part XII, Vol. III, Wiley, New York, 1959, p. 639.

149. (a) Meinke, W. W., *Chemical Procedures Used in Bombardment Work at Berkeley* U. S. Atomic Energy Commission Report AECD-2738, 1949 (OTS—$11.00, microfilm); *Addendum No. 1*, AECD-2750, 1949 (OTS—$2.40, microfilm); *Addendum No. 2*, AECD-3094, 1951 (OTS—$0.25). (b) Kleinberg, J., *et al.*, *Collected Radiochemical Procedures*, Los Alamos Scientific Laboratory Report LA-1721, 1958 (OTS)—$1.50). (c) Lindner, M., *Radiochemical Procedures in Use at University of*

California Radiation Laboratory (Livermore), University of California Radiation Laboratory Report UCRL-4377, 1954. (Publication Board Project, Library of Congress—$6.50 photoprint, $2.75, microfilm). (d) Murin, A., V. D. Nefedov, and I. A. Yutlandov, *Usp. Khim.*, **24**, 527–574 (1955); English translation in Atomic Energy Research Establishment Report AERE Lib/Trans 722, 1956 (The Librarian, Atomic Energy Research Establishment, Harwell, Didcot, Berkshire, England). (e) Finston, H., and J. Miskel, *Ann. Rev. Nucl. Sci.*, **5**, 269 (1955).

150. Millman, J., and H. Taub, *Pulse and Digital Circuits*, McGraw-Hill, New York, 1956, Chapter 11.

151. Momyer, F. F., Jr., and E. K. Hyde, *J. Inorg. Nucl. Chem.*, **1**, 274 (1955).

152. Moore, F., *Liquid–Liquid Extraction with High-Molecular Weight Amines*, National Academy of Sciences–National Research Council, Nuclear Science Series NAS-NS-3101, 1960 (OTS—$1.00).

153. Moore, R. H., and R. K. Zeigler, *The Solution of the General Least Squares Problem With Special Reference to High-Speed Computers*, Los Alamos Scientific Laboratory Report LA-2367, 1960 (OTS—$2.25).

154. Morgan, K. Z., "Techniques of Personnel Monitoring and Radiation Surveying," in A. H. Snell, Ed., *Nuclear Instruments and Their Uses*, Wiley, New York, 1962, p. 391.

155. Morrison, G. H., and H. Freiser, *Solvent Extraction in Analytical Chemistry*, Wiley, New York, 1957.

156. Morrison, P., "A Survey of Nuclear Reactions" in E. Segré, Ed., *Experimental Nuclear Physics*, Part VI, Vol. II, Wiley, New York, 1953, p. 1.

157. Morrison, P., and L. I. Schiff, *Phys. Rev.*, **58**, 24 (1940).

158. Mössbauer, R. L., *Z. Naturforsch.*, **14a**, 211 (1959).

159. Mott, N. F., *Proc. Roy. Soc. (London)*, **A124**, 425 (1929); Mott, N. F., and H. S. W. Massey, *Theory of Atomic Collisions*, Oxford, 1948.

160. Mott, W. E., and R. B. Sutton, "Scintillation and Cerenkov Counters" in S. Flügge, Ed., *Handbuch der Physik*, Volume XLV, Springer, Berlin, 1958, p. 86.

161. Murray, R. B., "Scintillation Counters" in A. H. Snell, Ed., *Nuclear Instruments and Their Uses*, Vol. I, Wiley, New York, 1962, p. 82.

162. Nelms, A. T., *Graphs of the Compton-Energy Angle Relationship and the Klein-Nishina Formula from 10 Kev to 500 Mev*, National Bureau of Standards Circular 542 (OTS—$0.55).

163. O'Kelley, G. D., in L. C. L. Yuan and C. S. Wu, Eds., *Methods of Experimental Physics*, Vol. 5, Part A, Academic Press, New York, 1961, p. 411f, and p. 616f.

164. O'Kelley, G. D., reference 163, p. 431.

165. O'Kelley, G. D., N. H. Lazar, and E. Eichler, *Phys. Rev.*, **101**, 1059 (1956).

166. Overman, R. T., and H. M. Clark, *Radioisotope Techniques*, McGraw-Hill, New York, 1960.

167. Overman, R. T., and H. M. Clark, reference 166, Chapter 5.

168. Owen, G. E., and H. Primakoff, *Phys. Rev.*, **74**, 1406 (1948); *Rev. Sci. Instr.*, **21**, 447 (1950).

169. Pate, B. D., and L. Yaffe, *Can. J. Chem.*, **33**, 610 (1955).

170. Pate, B. D., and L. Yaffe, *Can. J. Chem.*, **34**, 265 (1956).

171. Pate, B. D., and L. Yaffe, *Can. J. Chem.*, **33**, 929 (1955).

172. Pate, B. D., and L. Yaffe, *Can. J. Chem.*, **33**, 1656 (1955).

173. Paul, E. B., and R. L. Clarke, *Can. J. Phys.*, **31**, 267 (1953).

174. Peacock, W. C., and others, Ed., *Measurements and Standards of Radioactivity, Proceedings of an Informal Conference*, Easton, Md., October 9–11, 1957. (Nuclear

Science Series Report No. 24, NRC Pub. No. 573), National Academy of Sciences–National Research Council, Washington, D. C., 1958.

175. Peele, R. W., and T. A. Love, in *Applied Nuclear Physics Annual Progress Report for Period Ending September 1, 1957*, Oak Ridge National Laboratory Report ORNL-2389, 1958, pp. 249–259 (OTS—$6.50).

176. Pell, E. M., *J. Appl. Phys.*, **31**, 291 (1960).

177. Perkins, R. W., J. M. Nielsen, and R. N. Diebel, *Rev. Sci. Instr.*, **31**, 1344 (1960).

178. Perlman, I., *Nucleonics*, **7** (2), 3 (1950).

179. Perlman, I., and F. Asaro, *Ann. Rev. Nucl. Sci.*, **4**, 157 (1954).

180. Pleasanton, F., and A. H. Snell, *Proc. Roy. Soc.* (*London*), **A241**, 141 (1957).

181. Price, W. J., *Nuclear Radiation Detection*, McGraw-Hill, New York, 1958.

182. Reference 181, Chapter 7.

183. Reference 181, Chapter 4.

184. Reference 181, Chapter 6.

185. Reference 181, Chapter 5.

186. Reference 181, Chapter 10.

187. *Proceedings of the Amsterdam Conference on Nuclear Reactions*, July, 1956 [*Physica*, **22**, 941–1196 (1956)].

188. *Proceedings of the Symposium on Metrology of Nuclides*, International Atomic Energy Agency, Vienna, Austria, Oct. 14–16, 1959, International Publications, New York, 1960.

189. Putman, J. L., "Gamma-Ray Measurements and Standards," in G. G. Manov and W. L. Peacock, Eds., *Measurements and Standards of Radioactivity, Proceedings of an Informal Conference*, Easton, Md., October 9–11, 1957. (Nuclear Science Series Report, No. 24, NRC Pub. No. 573), National Academy of Sciences–National Research Council, Washington, D. C., 1958, p. 69.

190. Putman, J. L., *Brit. J. Radiol.*, **23**, 46 (1950), and in K. Siegbahn, Ed., *Beta- and Gamma-Ray Spectroscopy*, North Holland Publishing Company, Amsterdam, 1955, Chapter XXVI.

191. Reines, F., and C. L. Cowan, Jr., *Phys. Rev.*, **113**, 273 (1959).

192. *Report on Committee II, on Permissible Dose for Internal Radiation, 1958 Revision*, International Commission on Radiological Protection, Pergamon Press, London, England, 1959, and *Health Phys.*, **3**, 1 (1960).

193. Robinson, R. L., and L. M. Langer, *Phys. Rev.*, **109**, 1255 (1958).

194. Robinson, H. P., "Alpha Standards," in G. G. Manov and W. C. Peacock, Eds., *Measurements and Standards of Radioactivity, Proceedings of an Informal Conference*, Easton, Md., October 9–11, 1957. (Nuclear Science Series Report, No. 24, NRC Pub. No. 573). National Academy of Sciences–National Research Council, Washington, D. C., 1958, p. 2.

195. Rochlin, R. S., *Nucleonics*, **17** (1) 54 (1959).

196. Rose, M. E., *Phys. Rev.*, **91**, 610 (1953).

197. Rose, M. E., *Internal Conversion Coefficients*, North Holland Publishing Company, Amsterdam, 1958.

198. Rossi, B., and H. H. Staub, *Ionization Chambers and Counters*, McGraw-Hill, New York, 1949.

199. Rutherford, E., *Phil. Mag.*, **47**, 277 (1924).

200. Sattizahn, J. E., J. D. Knight, and M. Kohn, *J. Inorg. Nucl. Chem.*, **12**, 206 (1960).

201. Schumacher, E., and H. J. Streiff, *Helv. Chim. Acta*, **41**, 824 (1958); **41**, 1771 (1958).

202. Segré, E., Ed., *Experimental Nuclear Physics*, Vols. I, II, and III, Wiley, New York, 1953, 1953, 1959.

203. Seliger, H. H., and L. Cavallo, *J. Res. Natl. Bur. Std.*, **47**, 41 (1951); W. B. Mann and H. H. Seliger, *ibid.*, **50**, 197 (1953).

204. Seliger, H. H., and A. Schwebel, *Nucleonics*, **12** (7), 54 (1954).

205. Shive, J. N., *The Properties, Physics, and Design of Semiconductor Devices*, Van Nostrand, Princeton, 1959.

206. Siegbahn, K., Ed., *Beta- and Gamma-Ray Spectrometry*, North Holland Publishing Co., Amsterdam, 1955.

207. Slätis, H., "Source and Window Technique," in reference 206, Volume II, Chap. VIII.

208. Sliv, L. A., and I. M. Band, *Coefficients of Internal Conversion of Gamma Radiation*, Leningrad Physico-Technical Institute, Part I, 1956; Part II, 1958; Issued in U. S. A. as University of Illinois Report 57ICCK1 (Part I), and 581CCL1 (Part II) (Dept. of Physics, University of Illinois, Urbana, Illinois); *Soviet Physics JETP 4*, 133 (1957).

209. Smith, D. B., *4-Pi Geiger Counters and Counting Technique*, British Atomic Energy Research Establishment Report AERE-I/R-1210, 1953.

210. Snell, A. H., Ed., *Nuclear Instruments and Their Uses*, Vol. I, Wiley, New York, 1962.

211. *Source Material for Radiochemistry*, Publication 825, National Academy of Sciences–National Research Council, Washington, D. C., 1960 (free).

212. Staub, H. H., "Detection Methods," in E. Segré, Ed., *Experimental Nuclear Physics*, Vol. I, Part I, Wiley, New York, 1953, p. 1.

213. Steinberg, D., *Nature*, **182**, 740 (1958).

214. Steinberg, E. P., "Counting Methods for the Assay of Radioactive Samples," in A. H. Snell, Ed., *Nuclear Instruments and Their Uses*, Wiley, New York, 1962, p. 306.

215. Stephenson, R. J., *High-Pressure Ionization Chamber*, University of Chicago Metallurgical Laboratory Report MUC-RJS-2 (AECD-2463); F. R. Shonka and R. J. Stephenson, U. S. Atomic Energy Commission, *Isotopes Division Circular IDA-7*, 1949.

216. Stevenson, P. C., and H. Hicks, *Ann. Rev. Nuclear Sci.*, **3**, 221 (1953).

217. Stout, J. W., and W. M. Jones, *Phys. Rev.*, **71**, 582 (1947).

218. Strominger, D., J. M. Hollander, and G. T. Seaborg, *Rev. Modern Phys.*, **30**, 585 (1958).

219. *Symposium on the Chemical Effects of Nuclear Transformations*, Prague, 24–27 Oct. 1960, International Atomic Energy Agency, Vienna, 1961.

220. Szilard, L., and T. Chalmers, *Nature*, **134**, 462 (1934).

221. Tolbert, B. M., and W. E. Siri, "Radioactivity," in A. Weissberger, Ed., *Physical Methods of Organic Chemistry (Technique of Organic Chemistry*, Vol. I), 3rd ed., Interscience, New York, 1960, Part IV, p. 3335.

222. Uehling, E. A., Ed., "Penetration of Charged Particles in Matter," *Proceedings of an Informal Conference*, Gatlinburg, Tennessee, 1958. (Nuclear Science Series Report No. 29, NRC Pub. No. 752) National Academy of Sciences–National Research Council, Washington, D. C., 1960.

223. Van Rennes, A. B., *Nucleonics*, **10** (7), 20 (1952); **10** (8), 22 (1952); **10** (9), 32 (1952); **10** (10), 50 (1952).

224. Vegors, S. H., L. M. Marsden, and R. L. Heath, *Calculated Efficiencies of Cylindrical Radiation Detectors*, Phillips Petroleum Company, Atomic Energy Div. Report IDO-16370, 1958 (OTS—$2.50).

225. Villard, P., *Compt. Rend.*, **130**, 1178 (1900).
226. Wahl, A. C., and N. A. Bonner, Eds., *Radioactivity Applied to Chemistry*, Wiley, New York, 1951.
227. Wahl, A. C., R. L. Ferguson, D. R. Nethaway, D. E. Troutner, and K. Wolfsberg, *Phys. Rev.*, **126**, 1112 (1962).
228. Walter, F. J., J. W. T. Dabbs, and L. D. Roberts, *Rev. Sci. Instr.*, **31**, 756 (1960).
229. Wapstra, A., "Atomic Masses of Nuclides" in S. Flügge, *Handbuch der Physik*, Vol. XXXVIII, Part I, Springer, Berlin, 1958, p. 1.
230. Way, K., *et al.*, *Nuclear Data Sheets*, Nuclear Data Group, National Academy of National Council (Printing and Publishing Office, National Academy of Sciences–National Research Council, 2101 Constitution Ave., Washington 25, D. C.—$17 annual subscription, back issues available).
231. Whaling, W., "The Energy Loss of Charged Particles in Matter," in S. Flügge, Ed., *Handbuch der Physik*, Vol. XXXIV, Springer, Berlin, 1958, p. 193.
232. Wilkinson, D. H., *Ionization Chambers and Counters*, Cambridge University Press, Cambridge, 1950.
233. Wilkinson, D. H., reference 232, Chapters 2 and 5.
234. Wilkinson, D. H., reference 232, Chapter 6.
235. Wilkinson, D. H., reference 232, Chapter 7.
236. (a) Willard, J. E., *Ann. Rev. Nuclear Sci.*, **3**, 193 (1953). (b) "Proceedings of the Symposium on Chemical Effects of Nuclear Transformation," 132nd Meeting of Am. Chem. Soc., N. Y., Sept. 9, 1957; *J. Phys. Chem*, **62**, 1343–1389 (1958).
237. Wille, R. G., and R. W. Fink, *Phys. Rev.*, **118**, 242 (1960).
238. Wilson, R. R., and R. Littauer, *Accelerators: Machines of Nuclear Physics*, Anchor Books, Garden City, N. Y. 1960 (Science Study Series S17).
239. Wolicki, E. A., R. Jastrow, and F. Brooks, U. S. Naval Research Laboratory Report NRL-4833, 1956 (OTS—$1.00).
240. Yaffe, L., *Ann. Rev. Nucl. Sci.*, **12**, 153 (1962).
241. Yockey, H. P., "A Study of Aging, Thermal Killing, and Radiation Damage by Information Theory," in *Symposium on Information Theory in Biology*, Gatlinburg Tenn. Oct. 29–31, 1956, Pergamon Press, London, 1958, p. 297.

Subject Index

A

Absolute counting, 168–74
  of alpha particles, 168–71, diagrams, 169, 170
  of beta particles, 171–4
  coincidence (beta-gamma) counting, 173–4
  of gamma rays, 173–4
Absorption, 28–30, 33–43, figure, 29
  of alpha particles, 28–30
  of beta rays, 33–8
  correction for, in beta sources, 171, 172–3
  of gamma rays, 38–43. *See also* Gamma rays, interactions.
Accelerating tubes, 63
Accelerators, 62–7, Cockroft-Walton, 63–4
  cyclotrons, 64–5
  ion sources, 63
  linear accelerator, 65
  synchrocyclotrons, 64–5
  synchrotrons, 65
  target designs, 65–7, diagrams, 66
  Van de Graaf, 63–4
Acceptor, in semiconductors, 128
Activity, definition, 3–4
Add-one scaler, 161
Address pulses, in pulse-height analyzers, 161
Alpha decay, 12–15, barrier penetration, 14–15
  binding energy effect, 14–15
  Coulomb barrier, 13–15
  energy-lifetime relationship, 15
  general considerations, 12
  history, 13–14
  kinetic energy release, table, 15
  "tunneling," 14
Alpha particles, 28–32, 116–17, 126,
134–6, 168–71, 178, figures, 29, 135, 136, 169, 170. *See also* Alpha decay.
  absolute counting of, 168–71, diagrams, 169, 170
  absorption, 28–30, figure, 29
  delta rays from, 31
  detection, 116–17, 124, 126, 134–6, 168–71, figures, 135, 136
    with ionization chambers, 124, 126
    by scintillation counting, 116–17
    with semiconductor radiation detectors, 134–6, figures, 135, 136
  electrodeposition for source preparation, 178
  energy loss, of, 30–2
  range, 28–30
  range-energy relations, 29–30
  scintillation counting, 116–17
  specific ionization, 32
  spectrometry, 126, 134–6, figure, 135, 136. *See also* Ionization chambers, Semiconductor radiation detectors.
  straggling, 28–9
Amplifiers, 148–54, figures, 151
  blocking, 152
  clipping, 149–52, figures, 151
  delay-line clipping, 151–2, figures, 151
  differentiating. *See* Amplifiers, clipping.
  double clipping, 150–2, figure, 151
  double differentiation. *See* Amplifiers, double clipping.
  linear amplifier, definition, 149
  noise, 152–3
  pulse shaping in, 149–52

191